FIRST SHE FELT A WAVE OF SHAME, THEN THE STRANGE THRILL OF POSSESSION . . .

Never, never had she behaved like this. At first it appeared that he had meant only to brush her lips as they danced . . . but soon she was crushed against his chest, feeling the hardness of his strong, lean body as his mouth devoured hers. His lips on hers were passionate and persuasive. Her blood seemed to whirl through her veins, and she felt as though the only thing in the world was the man whose arms encircled her. . . .

HERITAGE
OF THE HEART

Nina Pykare

A CANDLELIGHT ECSTASY ROMANCE™

Published by
Dell Publishing Co., Inc.
1 Dag Hammarskjold Plaza
New York, New York 10017

Dell ® TM 681510, Dell Publishing Co., Inc.
Candlelight Ecstasy Romance™ is a trademark of
Dell Publishing Co., Inc.,
New York, New York.

ISBN: 0-440-13576-1

Printed in the United States of America

First printing—June 1982

Dear Reader:

In response to your continued enthusiasm for Candlelight Ecstasy Romances™, we are increasing the number of new titles from four to six per month.

We are delighted to present sensuous novels set in America, depicting modern American men and women as they confront the provocative problems of modern relationships.

Throughout the history of the Candlelight line, Dell has tried to maintain a high standard of excellence, to give you the finest in reading enjoyment. That is now and will remain our most ardent ambition.

Anne Gisonny
Editor
Candlelight Romances

*for the one
who showed me
Montana*

CHAPTER 1

The Montana sky was a brilliant blue and the July sun
warmed the bare arms of the slender auburn-haired girl
who stood feasting her eyes on the great old house, its
rose-granite turrets and arches speaking silently of another, older, time. Leslie Jordan motioned to the man who
stood patiently several paces away from her. "This one,
Paul. I want this one."

Paul Anderson lifted his camera and nodded cheerfully.
"Okay, boss lady. Just as you say."

Leslie Jordan smiled, the laugh lines crinkling around
her blue-green eyes. "Never mind the flattery, Paul. Just
get me some good shots. Be sure to get those turrets and
the arches. They're special."

Pushing his fair hair out of his eyes, Paul Anderson
went about his task, and Leslie turned back to the house,
a smile on her heart-shaped face. It was a face many men
had found attractive. Not beautiful. Her nose was too
uptilted and too liberally sprinkled with freckles for that.
But there was a charm about her, a liveliness and interest
in life that gleamed in her eyes.

On this particular morning she seemed perpetually
smiling. This article on historic Helena had made the
dream of her girlhood possible at last. As she gazed unsee-
ingly at the great house, Leslie slipped back in memory to
that day so long ago. In her mind's eye she saw the young
girl, her red pigtails dangling down her back, sitting in the

attic of the old house in Cleveland, staring at the diary she clutched in dirty hands. She had been ten years old then, ten years old and mourning the death of her mother. Left alone and motherless, she had clung to that old diary as a lifeline to the past. The past was all she had had then— the past and a father whose grief stopped him from seeing his child's loneliness.

"Hey, Les." Paul Anderson's cheerful voice called her back to the present.

"Yes, Paul? Isn't it something?"

Anderson shrugged. Having already traveled several times around the world, he no longer waxed particularly enthusiastic over new scenery. "It's okay, I guess. A good example of Victorian Romanesque. But why get so excited?"

"Oh, Paul, don't be such a wet blanket," she chaffed. "Look at this house. It used to belong to T. C. Power. He mined the granite from his own quarry."

Paul grinned. "I don't know how you could learn all that stuff about Montana so fast."

"Oh, I'm a fast learner," Leslie replied. "Power was a big shot in Montana, a merchant prince, one of Montana's first two senators."

Paul shrugged. "You did your homework, all right."

Leslie smiled. "That's my job. This article needs a little meat." She considered the man beside her. This was not her first assignment with Paul, and she found him easy to work with, not temperamental and touchy like some photographers.

"Well, *Vacations Today* sure picked a winner when they got you," Paul said cheerfully. "Do you have any idea how many stinkers I've had palmed off on me? Writers can be the world's biggest prima donnas."

Leslie laughed. "And here I thought photographers were bad."

He grimaced. "Some writers seem to think that I'm

10

psychic and can tell exactly what they want taken. 'Why did you shoot this?' they yell when they see the prints. Or 'I wanted a shot of that.'"

Leslie laughed again. "Poor put-upon Paul. Well, you needn't worry about me. I'll tell you. First we're going to get some shots of these old homes. I have a list here."

Paul shook his head.

"Then we're going downtown to look at the Governor's Mansion, Reeder's Alley. And the Golden Star Theatre." Her voice broke slightly in the middle of the last, but fortunately Paul did not notice.

Leslie swallowed a sigh of relief. No one knew how much this assignment meant to her, no one knew the joy that had filled her heart at the chance to come to Montana, a chance that was like going home. Years ago when the young Leslie had opened that diary and lost herself in the Helena of 1868, the dream of seeing Montana had been born. She had read them so many times that by now she knew the lines by heart. "I can't believe the sky out here," wrote Maggie Callahan, her exuberant great-grandmother, on July 10th, 1868. "It's so big and so blue wouldn't be anybody back East who'd believe me if I tried to tell 'bout it. And the country's so different. Some all bare and flat and lonesome, nothing but sage and buffalo grass. And other parts all hilly and covered with trees. Oh, I love Montana Territory. It's the greatest place in the world. But it's time to dress for the first show now. The Golden Star ain't the best theatre around, but it's decent and that's all a girl can ask these days."

"Les–lie!" Paul Anderson sounded slightly annoyed. "I said, I'm finished."

Leslie nodded. "Right. Sorry, I was daydreaming. It's just that these old places make me think about the past."

Anderson shook his head. "Don't they have any old houses back in Cleveland?"

Leslie managed a grin. "Sure they do. I've even done

11

articles about them. But there's something different in Montana. History is so—so close."

Paul grimaced good-naturedly. "Like all those historic signposts you're always stopping to read?"

Leslie nodded. "Yes, that's part of it, I suppose. The past seems so alive."

"You're a nice kid," said Paul with the mock wisdom of his thirty-two years. "But I think you've flipped."

Leslie made a face at him. "This is my heritage," she said, raising her arms to the sun. "My great-grandmother lived in Montana."

Paul's gray eyes surveyed her closely. "I think you're taking some kind of weird trip, Leslie, my girl. Just remember. The past is over. We live in the present. We have to."

"I know, I know." She brushed his advice aside with a carelessness that brought a furrow to his forehead. "But just think, my great-grandmother knew Mr. Power. She knew all the great men in Montana's history."

Paul's frown did not diminish. "She must have been quite a gal."

"She was. Oh, she was." Leslie took a hold on her enthusiasm. Paul had become a good friend during the time they'd worked together, but she'd better be careful with him. It wouldn't do to let old Richardson know that she was emotionally involved with this assignment.

She had a mental picture of crusty old Richardson: A small wiry editor with the loudest voice in the state of Ohio, he sat in solitary splendor behind the messy, battered desk, his dark little eyes shrewdly taking the measure of anyone with the effrontery to seek entrance to his sanctum. No, Richardson would bellow out something like, "Jordan, you blank blank little idiot, keep your heart out of this blanking business. People don't give a blank how you *feel*. They're looking for fun. Fun! Fun! That's

12

the whole shebang. Now get your tail out there and get me a story. A good story. You hear?"

Leslie turned to see Paul frowning at her. "If she was your *great*-grandmother, how come you know so much about her?"

She gave him a bright smile. "Family tradition." She hoped the lie sounded feasible; no one at all knew about the diary. It had been her own most precious secret—one she had not shared even with her father. She was not sure why no one in the family had ever spoken of Maggie Callahan. Perhaps they had been ashamed to have a dance-hall girl in the family tree. Or perhaps they hadn't known. When Maggie Callahan had left Montana with the man she later married, she left both her heart and her career behind her. That much the diary told.

Leslie turned east. "A few blocks will bring us to the other houses. Let's leave the car here. It's so nice we'll enjoy the walk."

"You'll enjoy the walk," grumbled Paul, gesturing toward his equipment, but he set out in the proper direction. "Do you really think those tourists will want all this historical stuff?"

"Oh, I don't mean to hit them over the head with it. Just a little, sprinkled here and there." She did not tell him that the need to see these places was strong within her, that she did not really care whether she used the material in the article or not.

Paul sighed exaggeratedly. "Well, my arches are good. And the sun *is* shining. So lead on, Macbeth."

Leslie chuckled. "Come on, Paul. I know you've been all over the world, but don't these old houses do anything for you?"

Paul grinned. "Sure. They give me nightmares whenever I think about heating them. Do you know what Montana winters are like?"

She smiled. "Pretty cold."

Paul made a face. "Pretty?" he echoed. "That's hardly strong enough. It's nothing for the weather to be below zero for days at a time."

"I know about the weather, Paul. The cold and the chinook winds. The whole thing. But I still love Montana. Look at that sun."

Obediently Paul looked. "Looks like any sun to me."

"Where are you originally from?" Leslie asked.

"Minnesota," Paul replied. "Why?"

"Because in Cleveland we don't have the sun like this. Not every day. Not so big and so bright. It's absolutely gorgeous."

Paul eyed her strangely. "This place sure does get to you. If I didn't know you better, I'd think you'd been hitting the bottle."

Leslie grinned. "You do know me better. No drinking on the job. But you'd better be prepared to see the inside of a lot of bars."

Paul's raised eyebrows gave him a puckish look. "Bars?"

"Sure thing. Some of the oldest back bars in the country are around here. The oldest in the state is in the Palace Bar at Havre. All glass and polished columns. It'll make a great shot."

Paul shook his head. "You're crazy, girl. Travel all that way just to get a shot of a back bar?"

Leslie wrinkled her nose. "Where's your sense of history?"

"Under good control," he said stolidly. "And not apt to get me in trouble like yours."

"Oh, come on," Leslie cried. "Don't be so stuffy. I know what I'm doing."

Paul's mouth curved into a smile. "Too bad Deadwood's in the wrong state. You'd love the chair that 'Wild Bill' Hickok was sitting in when he got shot. They have it preserved under glass."

Leslie returned the smile. "You're right. I would. But here we are. This is the John Boardman Home, built in 1889. See the Tiffany windows? The workmen knew the dimensions but didn't realize how the pattern went. By the time the windows came from back East, it was too late to change the frames. So they put the windows in sideways." She gazed up at the great house. "Imagine what it was like to live in such a place."

"I can't," said Paul. "That kind of elegance is foreign to my simple nature."

She made a face at him. "And here is the Hauser-Babcock Home. Twenty-nine rooms."

Paul made another face. Though he was taking plenty of shots of the houses, it was clear he didn't share her enthusiasm. "What," he asked almost petulantly, "does one human being need with twenty-nine rooms?"

"I suppose there were lots of house guests," Leslie said, her mind peopling the streets with carriages and women in long bustled gowns. "Travel was difficult then, you know. You didn't dash around in automobiles. When you got somewhere, you stayed for a while."

"I suppose so," Paul agreed. "But give me the present any day. The past is too slow for me."

"I wonder if you'd have been a photographer then, too, like L. A. Huffman."

Paul raised an eyebrow. "Equipment was pretty primitive in those days. Rugged stuff to lug around. And hard to work with." His mouth curved into a grin, but the gray eyes grew more serious. "How about a little fun tonight? There must be a disco or two in this burg. Live a little."

"You know I'm not a live-it-up girl." Leslie's smile was genuine, but it hid a real concern. She liked Paul Anderson, she liked him a lot. But not in the way he seemed to like her. There was no room in Leslie's life for romance. Men were all right as friends, but that was all. Not one of them had ever stirred a strong passion in her. And she

15

would have laughed had anyone mentioned the possibility of it. No, her impressions of men had been formed early—by the sight of a father lost in grief and by the tattered pages of an old diary that told a story of shattered love and hope.

"Yeah, I know. But you can't blame a man for trying." Paul shrugged philosophically. "We make a great team."

"Professionally," returned Leslie. "Speaking of which, we'd better get back to the car. We still have the old Governor's Mansion, Reeder's Alley, and the Golden Star Theatre to do today. Sometime, too, I want you to get a shot of Last Chance Gulch where they found the gold that started the whole thing."

"Just as you say, boss lady." Paul continued to smile, and if there was a lingering sadness in his eyes, Leslie did not notice it. Her thoughts were all for the Golden Star Theatre and what she would see there.

It was late in the day by the time they reached Reeder's Alley and the Golden Star Theatre. Leslie felt a big lump forming in her throat as she looked up at the old building. It was not very large, not as big as the Ming Opera House on Jackson Street, but beside the small stone and brick buildings that made up most of the alley, its faded brick exterior looked quite imposing.

Brushing the heavy hair off her forehead, she turned to the photographer. "Let's go inside."

Paul looked dubious. "Are you sure we can?"

Leslie laughed. "Of course I'm sure. I called. There's supposed to be a caretaker around. I wouldn't leave a thing like this to chance." She knocked briskly on the door. It was opened immediately by a fresh-faced young woman in blue jeans and a checked shirt.

"Come in. You must be Leslie Jordan. I'm Karen Hooper."

16

"Hello, Karen. This is Paul Anderson, my photographer."

Paul extended his hand. "Best-looking caretaker I've seen in some time," he said with a grin.

Karen Hooper laughed. "I'm not the real caretaker. George is over there, taking it easy. We're just cleaning the old place up."

Leslie looked around. "Why?"

"We're having a big benefit here tomorrow night. A masquerade ball."

"What's the benefit for?"

Karen Hooper's smile faded. "I don't know if you've noticed the rest of the Alley. We've been renovating it. Trying to return it to something like its original state. The Golden Star is part of the street. We don't want to see it go."

"Go?"

Karen nodded. "And if it does the whole Alley will be ruined."

"But why must the theatre go? I don't understand." Leslie's heart began to pound. They could not destroy this beautiful old place.

"The Golden Star belongs to D and D, one of the city's leading businesses. And they're negotiating with a big conglomerate. They want to raze it and put up a modern glass-and-steel motel."

"Oh, no!" The cry came involuntarily from Leslie's lips. "They can't!"

Karen shook her head. "I'm afraid they can." She turned to the photographer. "Be sure to get some good shots. That may be all we have left of the Golden Star."

"But the benefit? And can't someone talk to this D and D? Who owns it?"

"D and D belongs to Rick Donovan."

The name went through Leslie like a knife. Donovan, the name of the man who had destroyed Maggie Callahan's young dreams. "This Mr. Donovan, is he an old Montanan?"

Karen nodded. "His great-grandfather struck it rich in the Gulch. Just an ordinary Irishman then, they say, but he became one of the state's richest and most influential men. The Donovans have had their fingers in a lot of pies."

Leslie swallowed over the lump in her throat. "Can't someone talk to this Mr. Donovan? Surely he must have some pride in his state."

Karen laughed, the harsh sound echoing through the old theatre. "No one talks to Rick Donovan. He sent out the word. No talk. Just bring a better offer. In the meantime he's probably up at Whitefish taking it easy in the sun."

"Perhaps Mrs. Donovan?"

A curious look crossed Karen's face. "There is no Mrs. Donovan. Though there are lots of contenders for that title. Probably half a dozen or so are up there with him now. They say Estelle Lamprey looks like she'll manage to bring him to the altar, but I have my doubts."

"You seem to know a lot about Mr. Donovan," Leslie said.

Again that curious look crossed Karen's face. "If you read the newspapers, you can't help but know. The Donovans are big news. But anyway, it looks like the only way to save the Golden Star is to ante up more than the conglomerate. Money speaks, you know."

Leslie nodded. Yes, she knew that. And so did Maggie Callahan. To her deep regret. "When is the masquerade?"

"Tomorrow night," Karen said. "That's why we're cleaning the place up. We'll have the kind of music they had in the old days—when they had hurdy-gurdy girls. And everyone is asked to wear period costumes."

"We'll take two tickets," Paul Anderson said, correctly interpreting the look on Leslie's face.

18

Karen coughed. "I'm afraid they cost $50.00 apiece," she said.

Paul grinned. "That's okay. I'm solvent."

Leslie sent him a quick look. Clearly he knew how much the masquerade appealed to her, but she wasn't sure about his buying the tickets.

"Well," Karen said, "that'll be fine. Tickets'll be sold at the door. And I'd better get back to work. Thanks for your help."

"Thank you," Leslie replied meaningfully. "And don't despair. We'll think of something yet. We can't let a place like this go."

Karen nodded and moved away. Leslie turned to the photographer. "I know just what you're going to say," he forestalled her. "But I like this old place. I'd hate to see it go." He grinned boyishly. "If you want to put some more in the pot, go ahead, but I intend to give them the hundred anyway."

Leslie knew when she was beaten. "All right. You win. Take some shots now. The balconies and the stage. And some close-ups of the carvings and decorative plaster. Then tomorrow night we'll get some shots of the people. Maybe do a little interviewing."

"Les–lie." Paul's tone held a warning. "Richardson will have your skin if you try to slip such crusading stuff over on him. This is supposed to be a purely factual piece."

Leslie shook her head. "Oh, Paul, this is important. This place can never be replaced. Don't you see that?"

Paul nodded. "I see it, all right. I also see that by the time your article gets to press the decision on this place will have already been made. And you will have risked your neck—and your job, I might add—for nothing."

Leslie put one hand to her throbbing head. "Oh, you're right. I wasn't thinking. But we have to do something. Think, Paul."

He smiled grimly. "It's too bad *you* can't get to Donovan. One begging look out of those sea-green eyes, and he'd give you anything."

For a moment Leslie paused. "Maybe I *could* get in to see him."

Paul looked puzzled. "Now I know you've flipped."

Leslie pursed her lips thoughtfully. "I'm not so sure. After all, I'm a writer for a national magazine. Perhaps I want to interview Mr. Donovan about some antiques. He must have some valuable old pieces. Maybe he even lives in a historic house."

"Les!" Now Paul was alarmed. "You can't do that. That's false representation. You know very well that Richardson doesn't want any personalities."

"*I* know that," replied Leslie. "And *you* know it. But Mr. Rick Donovan doesn't."

"Les, you're mad." Paul shook his head wearily. "Just think about this for a minute. He's not going to like it one bit when he finds out how you wormed your way in to see him. He's out of your league, Les. He'll chew you up and spit out the pieces. I'm warning you."

"I hear you," Leslie replied. "But I'm not afraid of Mr. Donovan. Not on your life. Who knows? Maybe he has no idea what his company's doing. Maybe he'll *want* to save the theatre."

"And maybe I'll sprout wings and fly," the photographer said in disgust. "You're fooling yourself, Les. And you're going to get hurt. Bad. This guy Donovan's the playboy type, interested only in chasing women and living it up. He's not going to give a damn about a lousy old theatre."

"Paul Anderson! How can you?" Leslie glared at him as though he had maligned a person she loved.

"All right, Les." Paul was definitely disturbed. "I've had my say. And I see it's no use. When your mind's made up, there's no stopping you. So let's drop the subject. For now anyway. Seems to me we ought to be thinking about costumes for tomorrow night."

Leslie's eyes lighted up. "Yes, you're right, Paul. Go get your shots, then we'll look for a costume shop."

Obediently Paul began to move around the theatre while a bemused Leslie dropped into a worn seat and began to reconstruct a costume in her mind. She knew exactly how it would look. For one night at least, Maggie Callahan and the Golden Star would live again.

CHAPTER 2

By the next evening Leslie had acquired all the parts of her costume. The sheer black silk stockings from the hosiery shop had been the easiest to find. A dance supplier had come up with the short red silk costume embroidered with black sequins and the long black half-gloves. He'd even added a scarlet feather for her hair. Black pumps and a black mask completed the outfit.

Leslie, surveying herself in the hotel room mirror, sighed deeply. So this was how Maggie Callahan had looked. From behind the mask her blue-green eyes sparkled, and she had rouged her cheeks and painted her lips a vivid red. The auburn hair that usually swung loose on her shoulders had been coaxed into heavy ringlets that fell from below the knot that held the perky feather in place.

Leslie sighed again. The red silk dancing costume molded her round young breasts and dipped low between them, revealing an alluring cleft. Her shoulders, rising out of it, seemed surprisingly white, and she was pleased that she had taken precautions against burning in the sun. The tiny waist and very short, flared skirt made her look very feminine and desirable, something she seldom thought of herself as being.

What had it been like, she wondered, to be young and beautiful in those old days. That Maggie had enjoyed the male admiration that came her way, the diary made clear. It must have been a heady business, Leslie told herself. All

22

those womenless men just waiting there, their eyes revealing their hunger. And then that one man—Mick Donovan. Maggie had described him so graphically. The tall frame, broad shoulders, and lean hips that even the tattered dirty miner's clothes couldn't hide. The rugged, sun-darkened face with the vivid blue eyes and wide sensuous mouth that could be so cruel. The mop of curly black hair that he habitually ran long, work-hardened fingers through. Yes, Leslie thought, she could almost see him standing there. How could any woman resist such a man? A man, as Maggie said, with the charm of the black Irish just oozing out of his pores and the gleam of the very devil in those wicked blue eyes.

A hot blush sped to Leslie's rouged cheeks. How madly Maggie had loved the wild Irishman. And how ecstatically she had described his kisses and caresses. With a stifled exclamation Leslie turned away from the mirror. She was being ridiculous. Mick Donovan and Maggie Callahan were long dead and buried.

Her main concern now was to convince Mick's great-grandson that the Golden Star should be saved. And that could not even be attempted until the next afternoon when, as Mr. Donovan's private secretary with the clipped English voice had assured her, she would be welcome to interview him at three o'clock in his office in the Donovan Block.

Yes, that would have to wait. Tonight she would have some fun. Another sigh escaped from between the bright-red lips. Fun had not been a big part of Leslie Jordan's life. At eighteen she had lost the father who had become almost a ghost; she would always believe that he had gone happily to rejoin the woman who meant everything to him. After that she had applied herself diligently to her schooling and her trade. And here she was at twenty-six in her third year on the staff of *Vacations Today*. And,

23

until she hit Montana, quite pleased with her life and work.

But now, she thought as she paced the room nervously, now she was tired of working. For tonight, she told herself, her lips forming the words silently, she would leave the sane and sensible Leslie Jordan in her hotel room. It was Maggie Callahan who, dressed in this skimpy costume, her long black silk-stockinged legs and white shoulders so shockingly revealed, was going out to enjoy herself in the company of men. The young Maggie, whose heart was still whole, and who could enjoy the admiration in a male glance, and deftly turn away the pursuit, while still keeping an admirer.

A sharp knock on the door caused Leslie to jump. She hurried to open it.

"Well, well!" Paul Anderson made the simple words express a great deal. "Are you sure I've come to the right room?"

Leslie's red lips parted. "Me name is Maggie Callahan, and I'm waiting for a b'hoy to take me to the dance."

Paul grinned, entering into the spirit of the thing. "Yes, ma'am. This here cowboy is raring to go."

The cowboy costume fit Paul. He was lean and well built enough to wear the brown leather chaps, vest, and boots with a sense of masculine abandon. The broad-brimmed Stetson sat on the back of his head at a suitably jaunty angle. But his face gave him away, Leslie thought. It was a handsome face, but it lacked a certain ruggedness —the crinkled lines and rough skin that came from over-exposure to the weather, the marks of a real cowboy. She smiled. "I'm ready if you are."

They drove the rented car from the hotel to the theatre. Leslie, drawing her lacy black shawl closer around her shoulders, shivered slightly. There was quite a lot of her exposed to the chilly night air. She felt suddenly very nervous, not like Maggie Callahan at all. "P–Paul, do you really think this costume is all right?"

He turned to face her. In the streetlight he looked even more in character. "Of course it's all right. Come on now. Loosen up and have some fun." His eyes glistened. "In that outfit you'll have all the men after you." And he took her hand firmly and squeezed it.

EVERYONE WILL PLEASE REMAIN MASKED THROUGH-OUT THE BALL the sign over the door read. Momentarily Leslie wondered why, but then she dismissed it. She certainly didn't want to remove her mask. It offered her a feeling of anonymity. It was silly, of course, since Karen Hooper and Paul were the only ones who knew her, but at this point logic mattered very little.

The theatre looked marvelous. The old wood and gilt had been polished. The chandeliers held bulbs designed to imitate gas lamps. And with the crowd of people, all in costume, Leslie could easily imagine herself in the past that was so familiar to her. She recognized a bullwhacker, his long whip wrapped lazily around his shoulder. A sheriff and a bustled lady, a gentleman in a Prince Albert coat and a dance-hall girl, walked by arm in arm. Cowboys, Indians, soldiers, stagecoach drivers, cattlemen, shopkeepers, fancy gamblers. Leslie even saw an occasional Chinese, his long queue hanging down his back. And there was a Calamity Jane, dressed in men's clothes and carrying a six-gun. Leslie grinned happily. "Oh, Paul, isn't this marvelous?"

A strange look crossed his face. "So this is what turns you on. I'll have to remember."

Her murmured "Oh, Paul" was lost in his next words. "Listen, I'm going to the storeroom. I left my stuff there earlier today. I suppose if you still want those shots, I'd better get to work."

Leslie nodded. "I do, Paul. I really do."

25

"You're on your own, then. See you later." And he moved off.

For a moment Leslie stood there, still lost in appreciation of all the costumes she saw. There was a Jesuit, and next to him stood an Abraham Lincoln and a General Grant deep in conversation. The crowd was quite large, and Leslie wondered if the stage could hold them all for dancing. Several cash bars were in operation along the side aisles, and it looked like food could be purchased in the orchestra pit, except for one little section reserved for the fiddlers.

The seats were bolted down, of course, but the round construction of the theatre's interior seemed to encourage the forming of little groups. From the sounds overhead the balconies had also been pressed into service, and Leslie wondered how many people were feeling the same sense of freedom and exhilaration that the costume and mask gave her.

Newcomers had begun to jostle past her, and she decided to move down the aisle. In a way it was unfortunate that she had asked Paul to work. He would enjoy it, of course, because, as he had told her more than once in that half-joking, half-serious way of his, there was no better way to meet an attractive young woman than to be carrying a camera. But now with him gone she felt a little strange and friendless. Most of the people entered as couples, and she could tell that in spite of the masks many knew each other. Well, she told herself somewhat soberly, she could always do what she had originally intended, take notes on the dance for an article.

With this in mind she studied the costumes again, hoping to categorize them for future reference. And then she saw him. He was at one of the cash bars getting drinks. His black leather chaps fit closely over tight black jeans, the black guns and holsters slung arrogantly over lean hips, black boots appearing below the chaps. A black shirt encased his broad shoulders and was topped by a black leather vest. A black Stetson pushed back on his head hid the color of his hair. But there was something about his stance, some pure masculine essence, that kept her eyes transfixed on those lean, intriguing hips.

The platinum blonde next to him obviously felt it, too, for she leaned toward him shamelessly, her low-cut gown revealing a great deal more than Leslie's costume ever could. The blonde's fingers sparkled with rings, and a gleaming diamond necklace shone around her slim throat. Her gown, of a deep royal blue, clung to a truly sensuous body, and Leslie felt suddenly that her own costume was a sham. That woman knew her body, knew how to use it to attract men. Beside her, even Maggie Callahan would have been an amateur.

Leslie told herself to turn away. This man and his companion were no concern of hers. But as her eyes went back once more to the man's lean hips and broad shoulders, a strange sort of weakness invaded her legs. It was such an unusual feeling that she paused to examine it. No man had ever aroused such a reaction in her before. In fact, she had always wondered what all the male/female fuss was about. At least, no man had ever threatened to turn *her* existence upside down. It must be the exciting atmosphere and her feeling of being so close to Maggie, she told herself.

She had just reached this conclusion and was smiling slightly at her newly discovered romantic tendencies when the man turned. It was too late to avert her eyes; his glance had already caught hers. She had a fleeting glimpse of curly black hair above the black scarf he wore as a mask; a firm, jutting chin beneath a bushy black mustache; and a half-open shirt front revealing a mat of crinkled, black chest hair. Then his eyes were catching hers, holding them, while something live and frightening vibrated between them. The smile froze on Leslie's lips, and she was quite unable to stop from blushing as finally the arrogant,

27

demanding eyes released hers to sweep over her figure in an openly speculative fashion. Before his eyes could return to hers she turned away, her knees shaking, to seek refuge in a crowd of newcomers.

It was certainly not the first time she had met such a man. Cleveland had its share of macho types. But never before had she felt such an intense physical response to a man. Everything about him was sensual, she thought. The cut of his shoulders, the swing of his hips, the curve of his full mouth, and those eyes that had held hers so temptingly, eyes that offered blatant invitation.

Leslie shook herself mentally. She had meant to have fun, to enjoy being an attractive female. But the look in those eyes was a dangerous one. That man knew the extent of his charm; he knew it very well. He was apparently willing to use it. And she had no desire to be one of his trophies.

After a few moments of sane deliberation, her legs feeling stronger again, she began to make her way toward the orchestra pit. She did not need a drink, but perhaps she would have a little something to eat before she went up on the stage to watch the dancing.

She was about halfway down the aisle when a hand on her elbow stopped her. "Hello," said a deep voice, and she knew from the strange vibrations the sound raised in her, whom she would see when she turned. And she was right. He stood there, towering over her, an amused smile curving his lips. "I said hello," he reminded her.

She knew very well that she should send him packing, but her lips refused to form the words.

"What's your name?" he asked, his hand still on her elbow.

It came out independent of thought. "Maggie Callahan."

His eyes twinkled behind the scarf—vivid blue eyes.

"And yours?" she managed to ask, every nerve in her body quivering because his hand still held her elbow.

He chuckled, a deep rich sound that warmed her. "You mean, you haven't guessed?"

She shook her head. It seemed incredible that this man had sought her out. Some of Maggie began to surface. "No, how could I?" Leslie was surprised by the light, provocative tone.

He grinned, revealing even white teeth made even whiter by the bushy black mustache. "Why, I'm the Kissing Bandit, of course. Can't you tell?"

"Bandits are dangerous people," Leslie replied.

He laughed, his fingers tightening possessively over her bare elbow. "Are you afraid, Maggie Callahan? A brave Irish lass like you?"

"No." The lie was prompted by the use of Maggie's name. Maggie would have met this man with gay banter and offered her provocative red lips for his kiss.

"Good." His hand slid down her arm to her fingers. "Come on. Let me buy you a drink."

"I thought kissing bandits were hit-and-run, so to speak." Again Leslie was amazed by the teasing tone of her voice. Her insides were in chaos, yet she was acting like a sophisticated woman of the world.

His eyes surveyed her with amusement. "Forward little thing, aren't you?"

Leslie shrugged her bare shoulders and wished that she hadn't when she noticed how quickly his eyes fell to the top of her costume. She felt the blush spreading up to her cheeks.

"How interesting," he said. "A girl who can still blush."

His eyes lingered on her for so long that she grew even more uncomfortable. "Can I have that drink now?" she asked.

"Of course, little lady. Just follow me."

As the crowd parted before his determined advance,

29

Leslie, her hand still imprisoned in his, wondered vaguely if she had taken leave of her senses. She had never been much interested in men and a one-night stand was entirely unknown to her. How would this man react if he knew that the woman who was following him so willingly was still a virgin? The thought almost returned her to sanity, but by then he had reached the cash bar and turned to smile down at her, and she knew that all her defenses had crumbled. She simply could not walk away from him. It was beyond her power.

She accepted the drink he put in her hand and let him lead her away. "Are you new in town?" he asked. "I'm sure I'd have remembered seeing you before."

"You're acquainted with all the young women in Helena?" she asked, sipping her drink.

Again his laugh rang out, hearty and male. "All the beautiful ones."

"Really." Leslie looked him over with the same sort of predatory scrutiny he had given her. "You must lead a busy life."

"I do," he replied cheerfully. "It's amazing how many beautiful women find their way to Helena."

"I'm surprised you have time for them all," she replied, hearing the slight tinge of acid in her voice.

For a long moment he stared down at her. Then he laughed again. "I'm strong and healthy, well over twenty-one, over thirty, in fact, and they do say exercise is good for a man."

The invitation in his eyes was so blatant, it almost took her breath away. To avoid his look, she hastily swallowed down her drink. Silently he took the empty glass from her fingers and set it down beside his. Then he pulled her toward the stage where the fiddlers had begun to play. "This is a ball, remember? Let's dance."

She knew a moment of panic—how would she respond to the feel of this man's arms encircling her? Would she be able to control the responses of a body that seemed increasingly perplexing to her? But she had no time for hesitation; his hand had recaptured hers, and he was pulling her toward the stage. A rowdy kind of polka was going on, and dancers stomped and whirled gleefully. He leaned toward the nearest fiddler, and Leslie saw a bill pass from his hand to the musician's.

In a moment the polka had ended, and the tantalizing strains of a waltz began to fill the old theatre. "That's more like it," said the bandit, drawing her into his arms.

Leslie felt as though her legs were two dangling lumps, but then she became aware of the pressure of his hand on the small of her back, of his chest so close to her, the firm chin just even with her eyes, and all thought seemed to leave her as sensation after sensation washed over her. She felt as though she had no will of her own, as though every particle of her being was attuned to this man, this stranger who seemed to control her. Round and round the stage they went. Leslie clung to him, her eyes shut, her feet moving automatically.

She felt his warm breath on her ear, and a shiver went tingling down her spine. "Open your eyes," he whispered, his lips brushing her earlobe. Leslie was all sensation, every cell in her body fully aware of the male animal that held her so close. "Open your eyes, or I'll take my kiss now."

Her eyes flew open with a start, and he chuckled. "Usually my kisses are in demand."

"Then you shouldn't threaten people with them." She managed to get the words past suddenly dry lips. "Otherwise they might mistake the carrot for the stick."

The full lips so near her own smiled sardonically. "So kisses can be a punishment for you?"

"For any woman," Leslie retorted. "Because they're bigger, and physically stronger men think they can run women."

"And if their strength doesn't work?"

Her eyes sparked. "Then they use their kisses. Some as rewards. Some as punishment."

"I see. And how do you suppose my kisses would be for you?" he asked conversationally, as he continued to whirl her around the floor.

In spite of her heart pounding in her throat, she managed a bright little laugh. "That's hard to say, Mr. Bandit. *You* obviously think they're pretty special."

He grinned. "I haven't been getting any complaints."

"Then, why did you threaten me?"

"It seemed to go with the character. Kissing bandits didn't stop to make polite conversation, you know. They just took what they wanted. And I've got to admit that those red lips so close to mine are very tempting."

Without knowing what she did, Leslie raised her chin, offering him those lips. For one brief moment his eyes appeared startled, then he bent his head. As his lips met hers, Leslie knew what she had done, and a wave of shame threatened to engulf her. Never, never, had she behaved like this.

At first it appeared that he had meant only to brush her lips with his as they danced. But this teasing, tantalizing contact raised such a response in her that before either of them realized what had happened they were standing quite still, their arms locked around each other, while the dancers continued to whirl around them.

Leslie had been kissed before. And more than once by good-looking virile types like this. But never had a kiss had such devastating consequences. Her legs quite literally refused to support her, and without the strength of the muscular arms that held her, she would have fallen to the floor.

She was crushed against his chest, feeling the hardness of his strong, lean body as his mouth devoured hers. His lips on hers were passionate and persuasive, releasing sensations within her that she had never before known. Her blood seemed to whirl through her veins, and she felt as though the only remaining thing in the world was the man whose arms encircled her. His mouth moved on hers, his tongue forcing her lips apart, and she felt a strange thrill of possession.

How very good he was at this, she thought in passing, but it didn't matter that he was obviously an expert, that he had obviously had a great deal of practice. All that mattered was the feel of his mouth on hers. His tongue invaded her willing mouth, and hers retreated before it, until suddenly, without any decision on her part, it moved forward to mingle with his. Such a wave of longing coursed through her that she pressed herself even more avidly against him. She felt the heat of his hand on her bare back, and then it crept up to caress the vulnerable nape of her neck. The buttons of his leather vest bit into the tender exposed flesh above her costume, but it all seemed part of the ecstasy that was sweeping over her.

Finally the stranger released her mouth. "We're supposed to be dancing," he said against her hair.

"I know." Now that his mouth no longer covered hers she grew suddenly afraid. What had made her act like that—so unlike her usual self?

"Listen," he whispered. "It's getting awfully hot and stuffy in here. My car's outside. Let's go for a ride."

All kinds of warning signals went off in her head. "I–I shouldn't," she murmured.

"Don't go chicken on me," he said, his lips gently nibbling at her ear. "If you don't go with me, I'll have to kiss you again. As a punishment, of course."

"Of course." She wanted to make her tone light and saucy. This was obviously the time to say no. It was completely mad to go off with this stranger. Common sense and all her conditioning warned against it.

"Come on," he urged, his hand warm on the nape of her

33

neck. "Just a little ride to cool off. We're getting overheated in here."

She couldn't resist looking up at this last comment. And that was her undoing. Passion clouded those vivid blue eyes and pulled on her. Like his exuberant male body they exerted an almost magnetic attraction.

"I—"

"Just a little ride," he coaxed. "I promise to bring you back." And without waiting for an answer he moved off toward the exit, his fingers still holding hers.

Numbly Leslie followed him. It was almost like watching someone else. It could not be Leslie Jordan so willingly trailing this stranger, this Kissing Bandit. It was almost as if Maggie Callahan had come to life again.

They were outside before he spoke again. The cool air acted as a restorative, and when it hit her skin Leslie remembered. "My shawl. . . . I left my shawl."

"We'll be back," he repeated, stopping by a Mercedes Benz. "Get in."

"In that?" She knew her voice went up in a quaver, but she couldn't help it.

"In that," he replied, opening the door to a plush interior.

Leslie was about to protest again, but his hands reached out to help her and she climbed hastily into the car. As he moved around to get in his side, she experienced a momentary urge to fling herself from the car and run for her life. But she remained sitting there. She was not afraid of the tall, slim man who folded his body into the seat beside her and threw his Stetson in the back. Her madly pounding heart and her dry mouth were caused by fear of herself, a part of herself that she had not known before, suddenly come alive.

The Kissing Bandit had certainly chosen an apt costume, she thought with a touch of wry humor as the expensive car purred away from the curb. A man like this had no need for physical force. Women probably swarmed over him.

She jumped as his warm hand settled on her silk-clad knee. "Relax, Maggie. I don't bite . . . much." He grinned. "Have you been up to Mount Helena at night?"

"No." The word was a mere whisper. Her heart was pounding so loudly, she thought surely he must be able to hear it.

"The view from there is lovely. You can see the city all aglow with lights. Sometimes I go up there alone and sit looking down."

"Alone?" Leslie could not quite hide her astonishment.

He nodded. "Sometimes when I'm lonely I sit up there. And I imagine that each light shines from a home full of joy and laughter."

There was a strange wistful quality to his voice, but in the light of the dashboard all she could see was his profile.

For a moment Leslie hesitated. The man appeared to have everything. Good looks and wealth, at least. "Have you no home of your own?" she asked softly.

He turned to her then, and in the muted light his twisted features looked almost malevolent. "Of course," he replied harshly. "Several. One in Helena, one in Whitefish, one in Bozeman."

"You're talking about houses, not homes," Leslie returned, forgetting her sexual feelings in a wave of compassion for the agony she saw in that dark face. "Perhaps you should marry."

He shook his head. "Nothing doing, doll. Today's women are all the same—greedy and grasping." He pulled the car off the road and switched off the headlights.

"Women are not all the same," Leslie protested, not really angry because she had heard the hurt behind his words.

"No?" He swung toward her, his eyes dark and menacing. "They all want money. Even the ones who say they

35

only want fun. They expect the things that money can buy."

His arm snaked along the back of the seat and settled across her bare shoulders. A shiver sped over her.

"I'm a woman," she pointed out.

His frown faded to be replaced by a rakish grin. "So I've noticed." His fingers caressed her bare shoulder.

"I mean . . ." She was trying to resist the urge to move closer to that blatantly male body. "I mean, I don't look for money from a man."

He shook his head. "You're here."

She was beginning to get irritated. "I don't even know who you are. And I didn't know anything about this car until we got outside the theatre."

His mouth curved into a sardonic smile. "So you're a fun girl, Maggie Callahan."

"No—I—" Leslie stopped, unable to continue.

"Enough talk," he said, his fingers pulling her roughly against him. Her protesting hands slid into the open front of his shirt and her fingers moved against the crisply curling hair to the warm flesh beneath. A small sigh escaped her.

"Don't I get to see your face?" she whispered against his chest, the heady scent of male flesh overpowering her senses.

"No, Maggie. Let me remain the Kissing Bandit." His voice was hoarse with emotion. "Just once let me believe that it's only me that's wanted."

"It is." She raised her face to his, her eyes full of the longing that now possessed her fully.

"I want to see *your* face, Maggie. All of it." He drew the feather from her hair and tossed it in the back. "We won't need that." Then carefully he undid the mask. "That either."

In the moonlight his eyes were a deep, deep blue. Lying

back against his arm, Leslie felt his fingers softly outlining her features.

"Green eyes," he said, his voice a caress. "The eyes of jealousy." He kissed each one. "Red hair. The hair of bad temper." He pulled one curl teasingly. "A little upturned nose sprinkled with freckles. An Irish nose for an Irish girl." He kissed the tip of it. "And a stubborn mouth." He ran a fingertip over its parted wetness, causing her to press even closer to him. "Stubborn and tempting," he said hoarsely, his head bending to hers.

The world exploded for Leslie then. All she'd ever heard or seen about physical attraction seemed flat and insufficient beside the real experience. Why had no one ever told her how utterly enveloping these feelings could be? Like the tiniest drop of water falling into a whirlpool, she had no chance at all to escape the mad vortex of passion that enveloped her. Momentarily she fought to maintain her identity, her sense of herself, but she could not. Even that was swept away as she became one with the man whose mouth devoured hers so eagerly.

When finally he released her lips, she could only lie there. He kissed her cheek, his mouth trailing down her throat to the white mound that spilled up over the scanty costume. His lips sent little fingers of fire weaving through her veins. Under her hand she felt the mad beating of his heart as, unaware of what she was doing, she caressed his chest.

Raising his head, he pulled her closer into his arms. "Maggie, Maggie, my girl." His hand slid up from her waist, over the rounded curve of her breast, to linger teasingly on the flesh just above the costume. A deep sigh forced its way from Leslie's lips, and she felt herself slipping into a kind of sleepy lassitude. Expertly his fingers pushed aside the silk and curled around her breast. Then something else awoke in Leslie. From deep within her

37

welled up a yearning, and she twisted in his arms, her mouth seeking his.

That kiss, with his fingers wrapped around her flesh, was a revelation to her. She had been kissed before, and by experts, but it had never been like this. When it was over, her head drooped against his shoulder. His mouth moved eagerly down the curve of her throat to her breast exposed there in the moonlight. And another moan forced its way to her lips. She had not imagined it was like this, not when she had averted the frenzied fumblings of boys, or the more expert maneuvers of other men she had been with. One of his hands slid slowly up the silk-clad leg, up to where the black garters exposed creamy flesh, and she wanted to pull his hard body to hers and keep it there. His hands were strong, yet gentle, and her body responded to them in ways entirely new to her.

He raised his head, his eyes clouded. "I want you," he said thickly. "But this is not the place. I want time, Maggie. A whole evening. Time to do it right."

She stared at him. "I . . ." There were no words to tell him how badly she wanted him. And perhaps he did not need to be told. Shifting her hand, she had accidentally brushed against his growing hardness.

"I–I can't take you to my room." She finally got the words out.

"And the Bandit can't give away his hideout, can he?" His voice was still shaky.

"I suppose not." She sighed as his hand began to move again and lowered her eyes, knowing that her disappointment must be written in them for him to see.

He straightened suddenly and pushed her away. "Get yourself back in shape. I'll take you back to the ball."

"I don't want to go." She surprised herself by her frankness.

"Neither do I." His rueful smile backed up his words.

"But you know I'm right. This is not the place for it. And I want a whole evening."

She busied herself straightening her clothes, trying to put down the feelings that still clamored for attention. But she could not stop herself from asking, "When?"

He laughed. "Tomorrow night," he told her as he started the motor. "Can you meet me tomorrow night?"

She did not hesitate though she knew quite well what another meeting would lead to. "Yes."

"I'll get us a room. A nice one," he added. "Where shall I pick you up?"

"In front of the Desert Sands." It was not her hotel but it was close enough to walk to. This mad thing was not going to last; she knew that. And he would not be able to find Maggie Callahan in any hotel. *If* he ever tried to look.

"At seven." His voice sounded very businesslike, and she had a moment of fear. This was a ridiculous thing she was planning to do, entirely unlike her usual self.

It was almost as though he sensed her thoughts. "Eat first," he ordered, giving her that boyish grin. "I can feed you another time."

A laugh bubbled out of Leslie, a wild joyous laugh. So this was what it was like to be desired by a man, this wild kind of exultation. No wonder Maggie had loved it so. Of course, what Leslie was feeling for the Bandit was a purely physical thing. She told herself so, even then resisting an urge to put her hand back inside his open shirt. She would not make the mistake Maggie had; she would not allow herself to fall in love with a man. A brief fling, that's all it would be. And when it was over, she would resume her career, none the worse for the experience and wiser in the ways of the world.

The drive back seemed very long, and sitting away from the warmth of his body, Leslie shivered. He touched her knee briefly, then returned his hand to the wheel, gripping it till the knuckles turned white. "Don't worry, baby. I'll be there. If you knew how much I want you."

"I guess it's reciprocal," Leslie replied in such a woeful voice that he laughed.

"Come on, Maggie. You're a big girl now. You can wait till tomorrow night."

It was on the tip of her tongue to tell him that she had been waiting for twenty-six years, but she stopped herself. This was a man of the world; he might not want a virgin. She could hardly believe now that she had waited this long.

He pulled up in front of the theater. "Looks like the ball is still going on."

Leslie nodded. "Couldn't we go back in?" She couldn't bear the thought of him leaving her.

He shook his head. "Sorry, babe. I've got a big day tomorrow." He caught up her hand and pressed a kiss into the sensitive palm. Her senses went rocketing off again as he pulled her once more into his arms. But he did not kiss her. He held her for one brief minute, then turned to the door. "Back to the ball for you, Maggie." His face darkened momentarily. "Though I'd feel better if I took you back to your hotel. Too many men in there."

Leslie smiled. "They don't mean a thing to me. Who could compare a mere man to a mysterious Kissing Bandit?"

He grinned as he opened his door and came around to help her out. "Just hold onto that thought."

Leslie's fingers moved to the black scarf. "Will you take that off tomorrow night?" she asked softly.

His hand grasped her wrist with surprising strength. "Maybe." He looked down at her for one brief moment. "I've got to go. Till tomorrow, Maggie." And he bent and brushed her lips. Then grinning, he slipped into the car and raced away.

For a long moment Leslie stood there, watching the

receding taillights. Already the whole thing seemed like a dream. If her body hadn't still been filled with longing and frustration, she would have been tempted to think she had imagined it.

A faint movement behind her caused her to whirl. Paul Anderson stepped out of the shadows.

"What are you doing here?" Nervousness made her voice sharper than usual.

Paul looked down at the camera in his hand. "I came out to take a few night shots of the exterior."

"How–how long have you been here?"

"Long enough."

"I—we went for a ride."

"I see." Paul's voice was flat and expressionless.

"That–that was all."

"Leslie, I'm not your mother." In spite of his efforts to conceal it, she heard the pain underlying his words. "You're a big girl now and free to do as you please. Just"—he seemed to struggle with himself—"be careful. You're a nice kid. I don't want you to get hurt."

"I understand that, Paul." Leslie put a hand on his arm. "I know we're friends."

"Yeah." He could not quite hide his bitterness. "Friends." He swung toward her swiftly. "Leslie, listen, I've never told you. Maybe you don't know how I feel."

She shook her head. "It's no use, Paul. I do know. I've known for a long time. But it won't work. I don't feel that way about you. I value your friendship, but I don't love you."

"And I suppose you love *him*?" The words burst from him bitterly, and he seemed as surprised as she.

"No, Paul," she explained patiently, "I don't love him. And he doesn't love me." And then, because she knew she could not conceal the next evening from him, she added, "What's between us is purely a physical thing. Physical and nothing more."

41

Paul sighed. "I'd settle for that."

Leslie frowned at him. "Now, Paul, you know you wouldn't. Not really. You're too nice a guy for that. And, besides," she squeezed his arm, "we're friends. We can't regard each other as casual sexual partners. It would ruin our friendship."

Paul smiled grimly. "That's all fine and dandy," he said gruffly. "But what you're really saying is simple—I don't turn you on, and he does."

She did not deny it. He had seen too much. "I can't help it, Paul. *You* know that."

His smile turned wistful then. "Sure, no more than I can help wanting you." He shrugged. "Well, at least I'll be around to pick up the pieces."

Leslie shook her head. "There won't be any pieces. I know what I'm doing."

"Oh, sure, you make a habit of this kind of thing," he snapped bitterly.

Even in the semidarkness her blush was apparent. "Paul, you know that isn't true. I've never—" She stopped, realizing how she must be hurting him.

His voice was contrite. "I guessed that, Les. That's why I've been so careful. Not pressing you. Waiting." His voice changed and grew bitter again. "And now this guy comes along and—"

His voice broke and without thinking she threw her arms around him. "Oh, Paul, I am sorry. So sorry."

"I know." He buried his face in her throat and then, before she knew how it had happened, he was kissing her. She did not try to resist him. It wasn't necessary. There was no answering response in her, nothing but compassion for this man she was helpless to keep from hurting. She stood quietly until he released her.

"Well," he said with false cheerfulness, "you can't blame a guy for trying."

"I don't," she replied quietly. "And I am sorry. You know that."

He nodded. "Sure, I know. Well, is it back to the hotel or in to the ball?"

"I want to go back to my room," she replied. "But you needn't come."

"Nonsense," he retorted. "I've had enough for tonight. If I go back in there, I might do something stupid. I'll just go along with you, if you don't mind."

"Of course I don't mind," she answered quickly. "We can still be friends. Can't we?"

Paul nodded. "We'll stay friends. That way I'll be around. Just in case."

She did not try to contradict him. The past few hours seemed so unreal, she could hardly believe them herself. But as she climbed into the rented car, she realized that her shawl was still in the theatre. "My shawl. I forgot my shawl."

Paul shrugged. "I'll pick it up in the afternoon. I told Karen I'd be down to help clean the place up. Since you won't let me go with you to see the great Mr. Donovan."

"You know why I did that, Paul. If word of this gets back to Richardson, I don't want you to be involved."

"I know." He reached over and squeezed her hand, and she wondered briefly how it could be that the touch of one man's hand could mean nothing, while another's could send her into ecstasy.

CHAPTER 3

The Montana sun woke Leslie early. For one brief second she wondered why she felt so wondrously alive, and then she remembered. She stretched luxuriously, feeling very soft and feminine, and then closed her eyes, the better to remember his looks. How clearly she could see him standing there at the cash bar, the tight jeans and shirt molding his muscular body, the leather chaps and vest giving him even more of a masculine air. She smiled a little. The way he wore that gun belt, slung almost insolently over lean hips, was enough to reach any woman.

For a moment the smile faded. There was no doubt in her mind that the Bandit had had many, many women. A man who looked like that, kissed like that. A sudden sadness came over her, but she thrust it aside. She was going into this thing with her eyes open. The Bandit was a user. There was no doubt of that either. And by his own admission he, too, had been used. There was nothing wrong in that as long as both parties knew what was going on. This way she could have the experience without getting hurt.

Under the light blanket she stretched again, her body reminding her in several subtle ways of desires she had never felt until the night before. Until then she had never responded to a man's passion in that way. Now that she had, she wanted the chance to carry through on it. No matter how badly Maggie's love for Mick Donovan had turned out, her great-grandmother had never regretted loving the man, and the descriptions of her feelings and of the hours she had spent with the handsome young Irishman were engraved in Leslie's memory.

As a young girl she had been bewildered by Maggie's words about passion and caresses, and then, as she had grown older, it had seemed to her that such men as Mick Donovan no longer existed. And even if they had, they were better avoided.

But Maggie's descriptions of Mick's hot kisses and caresses had registered far more than Leslie knew at the time. She realized that now, as she closed her eyes and recalled Maggie's vivid portrayal of the first time Mick had come to her room. Leslie tried to imagine what it would be like to have the Kissing Bandit remove *her* clothes piece by piece, his hands free to explore any part of her body. And how would *he* look, that muscular matted chest bared to her?

A delicious shiver swept over her. Tonight, this very night, she would know. And now there were things to be done.

Mentally she ran over the list. She must wash her hair, decide what to wear, and rummage through her suitcase for the diaphragm that Sally Purdue had long ago insisted on fitting her for. Sally took her responsibilities as a doctor quite seriously, and she had lectured Leslie sternly. "You're a grown woman, Les. With a woman's body and a woman's desires." Sally's round face was screwed up in a frown. "So you haven't got a boyfriend now, and you think you've no use for men." A little grin curved Sally's mouth. "You're just as human as anyone else, Leslie Jordan. And someday you'll meet a man who'll break down all your barriers. When that happens, I want you to have protection, right there, ready to use. This jelly has a shelf life of five years. I'll remind you when to replace it."

Leslie, though she could not imagine being barreled

over by a man, could recognize the general truth in her friend's statement. And, since she was not a good liar and she wanted to ease Sally's mind, she took the little case and carried it faithfully. It was there now, stuck in a corner of her suitcase. Leslie smiled; she would have to thank Sally. It would certainly not be pleasant to go about in a strange city looking for such things. And she had to keep her head and think about this practically; she could not risk the possibility of a child.

She smiled and stretched again, and her languorous mood having passed, threw back the covers and jumped up. She felt good just to be alive, she thought, pushing aside the curtains and feeling the heat of the sun on her body. She could never get enough of this sun. She smiled, stretching her arms toward it. Then she turned to the closet. What would she wear tonight?

An hour later Leslie was out on the street. There had been nothing in her closet suitable for a tryst with the Kissing Bandit, and on an impulse she had left Paul a note and gone shopping. She needed a gown worthy of Maggie Callahan, and now she moved from shop to shop, not knowing exactly what she was looking for.

And then she saw it. It was emerald green and silky, with a deep-slashed V neck, both front and back. It took her breath away just looking at it. It was not a Leslie Jordan dress—that was for sure. And yet she yearned for it. It was just the thing for a "fun" girl to wear to a meeting with the Kissing Bandit. Almost without her willing it her feet carried her into the shop.

"Yes, miss?"

The clerk seemed rather skeptical, and Leslie put on her most professional face. "I want to see the green gown in the window."

The change in her tone worked wonders: the clerk now responded with alacrity. "What size?"

"An eleven."

Almost in a daze Leslie took off her pantsuit and bra. This dress could not possibly be worn over a bra. As the cool material slid down over her bare flesh, a shiver of sensuality quivered over her. The clerk zipped it up and smiled. "It's *your* dress."

Leslie looked at the figure in the mirror. The deep front cleft revealed a great deal of her breasts. Could she actually go out in public like *this*? And yet it was really only one man who would see her this way. And he would surely like it.

"I'll take it," she said briskly, not even looking at the price tag. Thank goodness for her credit card. "And have you any lacy white shawls?"

"Of course. Right this way."

Back at the hotel Leslie hung the dress in the closet and stood looking at it. Never in her life had she owned—or even wanted—such a revealing dress. Well, it was only for a night or two. They would not be in Helena much longer.

A soft rap sounded on the door, and she opened it to let Paul in. "Where have you been?" His eyes were frankly worried.

"I went shopping. I left a note at the desk." She did not add that she hadn't called him because she wanted to go alone.

He shook his head. "I didn't go downstairs. When I couldn't reach you, I was too worried to think of breakfast."

"Paul Anderson, you've got to stop this. Come in and sit down. As soon as I check my clothes for this afternoon, we'll go get lunch."

"All right."

She heard the door close behind her as she turned toward the closet, but she did not realize that he was right behind her until she heard his sharp intake of breath. Then she realized that the green dress was plainly in view.

"So that's what you bought. Some dress!"

She pushed it hastily aside until she came to her white linen suit. "Shall I wear the blue blouse or the peach?" she asked, holding them both out for inspection.

"The peach," he said instantly. "It highlights your hair. You're seeing that man tonight." It was more a statement than a question. "That's why you bought the dress, isn't it?"

She nodded. "Yes, Paul." She hung the clothes back in the closet and turned to face him.

"Les, this is insane. You don't know this man from Adam. He might be a rapist. A murderer."

"Paul." She tried to keep her voice controlled, to not give in to the irritation she was beginning to feel. "Now you're being silly. The man's perfectly respectable."

"What's his name?" Paul demanded.

She shook her head. "That's none of your business." She was aware of how it looked to him, and it was an awareness she did not need or want. This was to be her one big night of madness and passion, and she resented his efforts to destroy it.

"I bet you don't even know it," he growled. "I saw that he still had his mask on. Come on, Les. Tell me the truth."

She frowned. "Look, Paul, I'm perfectly satisfied about this man. And that's all I intend to say on the subject. Now, I'm going to get something to eat. Are you coming?"

He nodded grimly. "Yes, but—"

"Please, Paul! No more." She felt her nerves on the edge of breaking. "I won't stand for it."

"All right, kid." He forced himself to smile. "I hear you. Let's go eat."

Throughout the meal Paul managed to keep off the subject of her evening plans. He asked instead about this afternoon's interview. "What are you planning to say to this Donovan?"

Leslie smiled. "I intend to be very businesslike. I'll just ask him outright why he wants to destroy a national landmark."

Paul shook his head. "This country is lucky not to have *you* as a diplomat."

Leslie smiled. "I've always believed in coming straight to the point." She couldn't tell Paul that since last night she had hardly thought of Mr. Donovan—or even the preservation of the Golden Star. Since last night her thoughts had all been centered on a tall, lean man in black clothes and the wonderful feelings he had so unexpectedly aroused in her.

"How are you going to explain that you got in to see him on false pretenses?" Paul asked. "This man is no fool, and his time is valuable. He isn't going to like it. I can tell you that."

"I'll just smile at him," Leslie said flippantly.

"Les!" Paul put down his coffee cup to stare at her. "Whatever has happened to you? This is a serious thing you're doing. Risking your job—maybe even your career. You know how vindictive Richardson can get."

"I'm sorry, Paul." She gave him a little smile. "I'll be very diplomatic. I promise I will. I'll remind Mr. Donovan of his heritage. And I'll ask him very sweetly to consider the group's offer. Did Karen tell you how much they have raised?"

He shook his head. "No. I gather they did quite well, but she seemed to think that this conglomerate was going to up its offer. In which case they've still lost." He frowned and ran a hand through his sun-bleached hair. "Shouldn't we be moving on?" he asked rather plaintively. "We haven't got forever, you know."

"I know, Paul. See if you can get those other shots today. We need the capitol and the historical museum, especially the old stuff. I plan to go by there after I leave Donovan. I'll meet you there around four. I'll tell you more when I get there. Okay?"

Paul nodded. "Okay, but we really ought to move on tomorrow. Richardson keeps an eagle eye on expense accounts, and he knows to a tee how long it takes to wrap something up."

Leslie smiled. "Dear Paul, I think you're the one who's changed. You've never been such a worrier before."

"You've never given me cause to be," he retorted with a quick glance at his watch. "It's time for me to go. I have to meet Karen."

Leslie nodded. "See you later. Have fun. Oh, and don't forget my shawl, please."

"Of course, of course." He gave her a rather dark look as he got to his feet and left.

Leslie sipped her coffee. It was too bad that Paul had to get so touchy right now. Then she dismissed him from her thoughts and gave herself over to the delicious contemplation of the evening to come.

The Donovan Block was just like any other block in downtown Helena. The buildings looked old, but they were well kept, their stone facades clean. Leslie, waiting outside the elevator, took a deep breath. The preoccupation of her thoughts with the evening to come had stopped suddenly, and she was hit rather hard by the fact that she was about to face a very influential man, as Paul had so clearly pointed out, under false pretenses. Men with power were not likely to be very pleased by such things.

The sudden vision of blue eyes and a smiling mouth intruded into her consciousness, and Leslie smiled. So what if Mr. Donovan lost his temper: she would placate him. She had faced difficult interviews before. And there was always the evening to look forward to. She inspected herself in one of the mirrors that lined the old-fashioned lobby. Yes, she looked fine. The white suit and the peach blouse set off her hair and yet seemed businesslike. Her eyes gleamed, and her skin seemed to glow. She had confined her hair to a knot at the nape of her neck, but little wisps had escaped to curl around her face. *I look desirable,* she thought in surprise.

Just then the elevator came, and she stepped into it. The third floor was given over completely to the offices of D and D. When Leslie stepped out of the elevator, her feet sank inches deep into a plush orange carpet. They sank so deep, she almost found it difficult to walk.

Across the large waiting room, behind a desk that reflected the sun's rays, sat an elegantly dressed young woman. "Miss Jordan?" came the clipped British tones.

"Yes." Leslie advanced toward the desk. The room practically shrieked of money. From the orange plush carpet to the peach walls hung with abstract art to the comfortable real leather chairs and the shapely young woman behind the desk, the room spoke of taste and elegance.

"Mr. Donovan will be free in a moment. Please have a seat."

"Thank you." Leslie lowered herself into one of the leather chairs. She removed her pad and pen from her handbag and, thus armed and ready, began surreptitiously to study the receptionist.

The blonde behind the desk wore an expensive suit, a suit of the palest blue that made Leslie's white linen one look as if it came off a bargain rack. Under the suit was a blouse of royal-blue silk, undoubtedly *real* silk. Leslie swallowed a sigh. Even the receptionist's hairdo was perfect, not a single hair out of place. She began to feel more and more dowdy and insignificant before this modish creature until a sudden thought of the evening to come made her smile again. There were lots of beautiful women in

Helena, as the Bandit had said. But last night and tonight he had chosen *her*—Leslie Jordan.

A buzzer rang on the desk, and a door could be heard closing somewhere on the floor. So, thought Leslie, a private exit, too.

"Mr. Donovan will see you now," said the blonde, her pretty mouth curving in an artificial smile. "Right that way."

"Thank you." Clutching her pad and pen, Leslie moved toward the inner door. Now she would see Rick Donovan, great-grandson of the man who had broken Maggie Callahan's heart. Her fingers did not tremble as they curled around the knob. The past was over and gone; if she wanted to enlist this man's help in saving the Golden Star it was best to forget the past altogether.

She turned the knob and stepped into the room. Noiselessly the door swung shut behind her. Leslie had the impression of a large room. The floor was covered with a deep-brown carpet that picked up the rich hues of the mahogany paneling. Behind a huge desk a row of large windows opened the room to the Montana sun. Here, too, everything spoke of taste. Quiet, masculine, moneyed taste.

In front of the center window, his back to her, stood a tall, lean figure. The sun behind him blinded her, but her senses stirred restlessly. There was something vaguely familiar about the figure. "Mr. Donovan?" She was glad her voice came out strong and clear.

The figure seemed to stiffen for a fraction of a second. Then he turned and came toward her.

The pad and pen fell from Leslie's lifeless fingers as she came face to face with the Kissing Bandit. Without the mask he was even more handsome. "You?" she breathed.

He nodded. "What are you doing here, Maggie? I have an appointment with Leslie Jordan." Those vivid blue eyes rested on her face.

52

Her pulse was pounding at the sight of him and she couldn't seem to think straight. "I–I am Leslie Jordan," she stammered.

"I see." His eyes grew cold and his jaw hard. "I suppose you're going to explain all this."

She nodded. "Could–could I sit down?"

"Of course." He gestured toward one of the chairs.

Feeling more and more the fool, she retrieved her pad and pen and sank into the chair. He settled in another, ignoring the desk. His lightweight suit of some cream-colored material contrasted vividly with his dark hair and his sun-browned skin. In a dress shirt and tie, he seemed a stranger. But the businessman's clothes did nothing to detract from his attractiveness or to decrease his blatant male appeal to her senses. He crossed long legs and seemed to relax, but Leslie knew better. Those eyes were scrutinizing her every movement and expression. "I–I hardly know where to begin," she stammered.

"You might try the beginning," he said dryly. "Why did you give me a false name?"

He made it sound like an accusation, and Leslie cringed. "I didn't."

"You mean your name *is* Maggie Callahan?"

"No."

His eyes were cloudy with anger, and his tone was clipped. "I suggest you get down to the facts, Miss Whoever-You-Are. My time is valuable."

"Yes, sir!" Leslie was beginning to get angry now. There was no need to make a federal case of it. "I wanted to have some fun, and I was thinking of my great-grandmother. So I used her name."

"I see." His tone was still cold. "And how did you discover *my* identity?"

Leslie was bewildered. How could he have changed so much? "I didn't. I had no idea my Kissing Bandit"

—her tongue stumbled over the words, and the color raced to her cheeks—"was Rick Donovan."

"Of course not." His tone contradicted the statement.

"But I didn't. How could I?"

He smiled, a harsh cold smile that sent chill fingers of ice into her heart. "I am rather a well-known figure around town. Any number of people could have pointed me out to you."

"But they didn't! I don't know anyone in town."

His harsh expression did not soften. "I am not a fool, Miss Jordan. After my secretary gave you an appointment, I sent someone to research your journal." His eyes were as cold as a winter sky. "As you well know *Vacations Today* carries no interviews. It is a publication about *places*. Now perhaps you'll stop wasting my time and tell me what you want from me."

"But—" Leslie was heartsick. She must somehow make him understand. "It wasn't like that at all. Really."

His expression did not change. "Miss Jordan. There remain five minutes of your appointment time. No more. Now. What do you want?"

She saw that it was useless; she could not explain it to him. "I wanted to ask you to help save the Golden Star. It's a landmark, a historic landmark. The group has raised quite a lot of money. Surely you can be satisfied with that. You have so much." She glanced around her. "You wouldn't even miss the extra profit."

He looked at her strangely. "You don't know much about business," he said sharply. "No one turns down a profit."

"You could." The words were a mere whisper. He ignored them.

"And if I don't let your friends have the theatre?" he asked.

"I can't believe you would be so cruel," she cried.

54

"Where's your pride in your home state? In your state's history? The Golden Star can never be replaced."

"How fortunate for progress," he goaded, his eyes challenging her. "But what a lot of trouble you've gone to for that old dump. Seduction and all the rest. I've heard of everything now. Imagine a woman willing to give her body to preserve a building!"

Leslie jumped to her feet. "I think you're crazy!" she shouted. "Until I walked in this room I didn't know Rick Donovan from Adam. I thought the man I met last night was a human being. I made a big mistake. You—you're just a machine. A cold brutal machine. And I wouldn't touch you with a ten-foot pole! And now Mr. Donovan, I'll get out of your office—and your life—so you can attend to your very important business!"

Almost blinded by the sudden tears that had risen to choke her, she turned and hurried toward the door. She would not stay in this room for another minute. But in her outrage she forgot about the thick carpet. She was almost to the door when one of her heels caught, and, taken off balance, she fell heavily.

She did not realize Donovan was following her until she felt a pair of muscular arms catch her. With a gasp she was brought up against his chest.

"Very neatly done," he said, his stormy eyes gazing down into hers derisively. "I believe you missed your calling, Leslie Jordan. You should have been an actress."

She was far too conscious of the arms that encircled her. His entire body seemed to give off vibrations, intense male vibrations that threatened to engulf her. "Let me go," she sputtered. "You're just another machine. A cash register!" She tried to wiggle free of his arms, but it was useless. With one arm he held her helpless against him while with the other he gripped her chin. She tried to twist away from him, but his grip was like iron. Tears of pain came to her eyes, but he ignored them.

"So I'm a machine, am I?" The words were soft, the tone deadly. "Let's just see." And he bent his head.

Leslie struggled with all her strength to avoid those lips, but her battle was futile. He took her mouth, not as he had before in tenderness and exploration, but savagely and harshly he ravaged the soft lips that opened so reluctantly beneath his own. His mouth bruised hers, forcing her lips against her teeth. She tasted the saltiness of blood. And then the hand that had held her chin released it and slid down inside the white suit, seeking the curve of her body. As his fingers tightened, Leslie tried to kick at his ankles, but he had one of her arms secured between their bodies, and the other he held tightly by the wrist. She was helpless under his experienced hand. Longing welled up in her—so strong she almost forgot her outrage, almost forgot that this was not lovemaking but punishment he was subjecting her to.

As he held her helpless, his mouth devouring hers, his fingers slid down over her rib cage, down inside the elastic band of her skirt, and Leslie stiffened as male fingers moved over the smooth skin of her belly. She fought him harder then, her breath coming in gasps. But her body threatened to become a liquid thing not her own, a pliant thing that arched toward him. In one swift movement he lay her back on the carpet and lowered himself on her.

She continued to fight him until she was breathless, but she could not escape him. His lips continued to hold hers, and her body could not help molding itself to him.

And then he rolled to his knees. His dark features pulled into a savage grimace, he loomed over her. She saw him only hazily, through eyes dulled by longing. "Now, Miss Jordan," he said coldly, the sound of his voice falling like ice water on her overheated body, "now, who is a machine? All it takes is a man to push the right buttons, and you respond immediately."

Shame lay on her and prevented her from replying.

56

"I doubt that you care to be seen leaving here in that condition," he went on, getting to his feet. He gestured. "Through there is a washroom. I suggest you go do something about your looks. The outer door from it leads to another elevator. You can go out without having to face my receptionist."

And he turned on his heel and left her lying there. Leslie heard the sound of the door as it closed behind him. Slowly she pushed herself to her feet and made her way toward the washroom. She felt incredibly tired, battered and weary. Hanging on to the washbasin, she looked at herself in the mirror. Her eyes were still cloudy with desire, her face flushed from his kisses. With numbed fingers she rebuttoned her blouse, tucked it into her skirt. Her hair had escaped its knot and hung in disarray over her shoulders. Her hands trembled as she lifted cold water to her heated face. The man was a brute, a vicious beast. More color stained her cheeks as she recalled his words. But she was not what he had assumed. She was not at all practiced at this. If she had been, perhaps she could have resisted him better. But when he reached those hidden depths, when he called forth parts of herself she had not even known existed, she could only fight so long. He could have had her there, right there on the plush carpet of his office. And he knew it.

Leslie combed and rearranged her hair. The man was also paranoid. All that fuss because she had given him a false name! Why, he hadn't given her any at all! What right had he to be so sarcastic? And then to believe that she had arranged their meeting at the masquerade. Such conceit.

She gave herself a once-over in the mirror. The high color in her cheeks was fading, and now that she was tidy again, the only sign of their encounter was the slight swelling of her lower lip. Fortunately the cut was on the inside.

If Paul asked, she could tell him that she had accidentally bitten herself.

Straightening her shoulders, Leslie opened the other door and stepped out into a little hall where an elevator waited. All the comforts of home, she thought dryly. Well, so much for Rick Donovan. They would have to save the theatre some other way. If money was all Donovan could see, then that's what they'd give him. Money, money, and more money.

By the time Leslie had reached the Historical Society building on North Roberts Street, she was feeling more normal. There was no denying what had happened, but she could not help thinking that any woman with blood in her veins would have responded in the same way. Flesh and blood could only withstand so much, she thought as she entered the large building across from the state capitol.

Then she pushed what had happened to the back of her mind. There should be something in the article on the museum displays she was looking at. The dioramas of buffalo and Indians were always interesting, cowboys and cattle drives, too. But Leslie stood longest before the gold-mining displays. Without any urging on her part her mind presented her with a picture of Rick Donovan in the grubby clothes of the miner. But no matter how she pictured him, even with dirty hands and marks of grime on that handsome, arrogant face, the attraction was still there. Maggie's Mick had looked like that, Leslie thought, in the days when he and Maggie had been so in love. But the streak of cruelty she had seen in his great-grandson that afternoon had been just as strong in the man who had struck it rich and then turned his back on the poor dancer who loved him. Turned his back to marry a rich society girl from the East.

"Leslie." She shook her head, Paul's voice bringing her back to the present.

"Hi, Paul. I just stopped to look for a minute. Did you get some shots of these?"

Paul nodded. "You should look at the Charlie Russell stuff, too. Boy, how that guy could paint. They've got a lot of his sculptures there and some of his personal letters to people. He always decorated them with drawings, you know." Paul sighed deeply. "What I'd give for such a talent."

Leslie looked at him in surprise. "Do you paint? I didn't know."

His smile was rueful. "I *want* to paint, but I have no talent. That's why I turned to photography. It's better than nothing." He grinned a little shakily. "Don't look so sad, my dear. I haven't let it blight my life. I think we ought to do some shots of the Territory Junction, too. I particularly like the frontier drugstore and the dentist's office."

Leslie shuddered. "Ugh! Still, you're right. We'll include something on it." She dug out pad and pen, her fingers trembling as she remembered where last she had held them. "Go ahead and get your shots," she said.

Paul nodded. "I've already spoken to the manager and got the okay." He gave her a shrewd, inquisitive look. "You *are* going to tell me what happened in Donovan's office, aren't you? I've been dying of curiosity. And Karen will want to know."

"He said no." Leslie managed to control her voice, but she knew that her cheeks were reddening. She turned toward the diorama of the beaver trade behind her and began to take notes.

Paul was not put off. "There must have been more to it than that. What was he like? How did he behave? Did he lay into you? Come on, give."

"Paul, please! This is not the place to discuss it. I'll tell you at dinner, okay?" The moment the words were out she knew her mistake.

"I thought—Aren't you meeting—"

Leslie sighed heavily. "No, I'm not. I've had a very difficult afternoon, Paul. Now, if we can just finish here, I promise to tell you all about it."

"Okay." His eyes looked worried, but he nodded. Then he grinned sheepishly. "Oh, about dinner. Since I expected you to be–ah–unavailable, I asked Karen. Comfort in misery. You know the bit. But now you can join us."

She started to protest, but he interrupted her. "Hey, friends. Remember? Besides, we'll both be dying to hear what happened. I'd also like to know why you changed your—" Something in her face stopped him. "Time to get those shots," he said, moving briskly away.

Leslie, fighting the sudden scalding tears, bit her already bruised lip and almost cried out in pain. She would have to tell Paul something of what had happened, though naturally she would omit the degradation that had ended with her on the floor. No one need know about that. She would even speak in front of Karen, she told herself. Perhaps Karen might have some explanation for Mr. Donovan's paranoia where women were concerned. And, anyway, the other woman was entitled to some explanation for Leslie's failure.

CHAPTER 4

That evening, wearing a long rust skirt and pale orange blouse, Leslie followed Paul into the fashionable supper club where he was supposed to meet Karen Hooper. She had not felt much like dressing up. Her first act on reaching her room had been to shove the green dress to the back of the closet. But common sense had come to her rescue, that and the knowledge that the club Paul had chosen was one of the city's best. She did not want to feel entirely out of place and when she saw the other people dining there she was glad to have dressed up, even if it was only a little. Her long dark skirt picked up the color of her hair, which tonight she had elected to let swing free. The pale orange blouse with its scooped neck and long full sleeves was feminine and yet not blatantly so. And a fine gold chain with its free-swinging heart shone against her throat.

The waiter led them directly to a good table. For a moment Leslie stared in surprise at the woman waiting there. Karen had shed her blue jeans and plaid shirt for a sophisticated dinner dress of sky blue that set off her sleekly coiffed hair. The sapphires that sparkled on her throat and wrist could have been artificial, but somehow Leslie doubted it.

"Leslie. I'm so glad you could come." Karen indicated a chair. "Do sit down. Paul tells me you confronted the ogre in his den, and I am dying to know what happened."

Leslie felt the color flooding her cheeks as Paul helped

her into her chair. "I'm afraid it's rather complicated," she said.

"You *are* going to tell us, aren't you?" Two pairs of eyes fastened upon her gravely.

Leslie nodded. "Yes, yes. Of course I am. But—" She forced herself to meet Karen's sympathetic eyes. "I have to back up a little. To last night."

"We're all ears," said Paul. "Go on."

Leslie continued to look at Karen. The warmth in the other woman's eyes promised understanding. "Last night at the masquerade I met a man. He was dressed like a bandit—all in black."

Karen nodded.

"We hit it off and we went for a ride. To talk," she added lamely. "And we made a date for tonight. He–he didn't tell me his name." She heard Paul's snort of annoyance, but did not look at him. "And when he asked my name, I told him it was Maggie Callahan." Karen looked puzzled, and Leslie hurried on. "It was my costume, you see. I dressed like my great-grandmother, Maggie Callahan. She was a dancer at the Golden Star. Back in Helena's early days. I have her diary. And–and I felt like her. Sort of—"

"Reckless," Karen supplied. "I understand that."

"I don't," Paul said, but at Karen's look he subsided into silence.

"Go on, Leslie," Karen urged.

"As I said, we made a date for tonight." The waiter came up then, and she sat silent while the orders were taken, accepting Karen's suggestions with a nod. Then the waiter was gone, and they turned back to her.

Leslie took a deep breath. "Today I went to speak to Mr. Donovan and . . . he turned out to be last night's bandit." She finished with a rush, pressing her trembling hands together in her lap.

"My God!" Paul's whisper was shocked. "So what was the problem?" he asked after a moment's silence.

Leslie forced herself to look at him. She couldn't keep avoiding his eyes forever. "Mr. Donovan did not like it that I had given him a false name. And—and he suspected that I had arranged to meet him the night before in order to wheedle him into helping us. He also knew about *Vacations Today*. That we don't use pieces on people. So he was doubly suspicious."

"But surely you told him the truth," Paul exclaimed.

"Mr. Donovan had no use for the truth," Leslie said heavily. "He insisted that someone had pointed him out to me and that I had behaved in an underhanded fashion."

"Did he say anything about Richardson?" Paul asked in a worried tone.

Leslie shook her head. "No, I don't think he'd bother. He's too busy a man. He just told me no and good-bye." She turned to Karen. "He seems to have some kind of paranoia about women."

Karen nodded thoughtfully. "He must have bought his ticket at the door. I didn't know he'd be there. It is a little peculiar." She smiled gently. "Don't feel bad that he rushed you off your feet. He does that to every woman."

There was something in Karen's smile that prompted Leslie to say, "Not you, too?" And she was not at all surprised when Karen nodded.

"We were an item a year or so ago. When I finally decided to get back in the social scene after Dan's death, Donovan appeared. My husband's death left me quite a rich woman, and so Rick didn't have to worry about me being a gold digger. But then he discovered that I did want something from him." Karen sent Paul a curious kind of glance. "I'm not a playgirl. I value security and home life. Donovan wasn't ready for that. So we called it quits."

Leslie's face reflected her bewilderment. "But why is he like that? Do you know?"

Karen's eyes grew serious. "He didn't tell me. He's very closemouthed about himself. But I heard it through the grapevine. It seems that when he was very young, he was madly in love with a cocktail waitress. His parents sent him off to Europe for the summer. The girl promised to wait, but the father bought her off, and she married someone else. They say when Rick got back, he just about tore the place apart. Since then he's been convinced that all women are alike."

"And when he meets one who isn't?" asked Leslie.

Karen shrugged. "He believes the worst anyway. A man in his position, with his looks and his money. You can hardly blame him for being suspicious, I guess. And he certainly has no problem finding women who are willing to live up—or down—to his idea of them."

Leslie nodded. No wonder he had thought so poorly of her.

"Speaking of which," said Karen sotto voice, "here he comes now. And with another playmate."

Leslie refused to turn her head; she kept her eyes on her plate until Donovan and his companion had passed by the table. Then she could not resist looking up. Her heart skipped a beat at the sight of his broad back. He was wearing a lightweight suit that fit his body to perfection, and the dark hair curling over his coat collar made her heart wrench with longing. The blonde hanging on his arm was the same one she had seen with him at the masquerade. The bright hair and provocatively swinging hips could not be mistaken.

"Estelle Lamprey," Karen whispered. "She has money, too."

Leslie nodded. And an empty head, she added silently. It seemed clear that Mr. Donovan had no use for a woman with brains or any kind of deeper feelings. Leslie returned her eyes to her plate. Rick Donovan was no concern of hers; she meant to wash all remembrance of him out of her mind.

"Uh-oh!" Paul's sound of dismay made her raise her head.

"What's wrong?"

"They've taken the table which is two across from us. He's going to be looking right at you. Do you want to move around here?"

Leslie shook her head, her heart pounding. "Of course not. I'm not afraid of the man. Now, Karen, how much do you think the conglomerate will hike its bid?"

Karen frowned. "I don't really know. But they have plenty of assets."

"Maybe some of the city's wealthier people—" Leslie began.

Karen shook her head. "I'm afraid not, Leslie. There are quite a few of Helena's more fortunate citizens interested in saving the Golden Star. That's why we were able to make Donovan an offer at all. But most of us have given as much as we can. A lot of our capital is tied up in stocks, and with the market the way it is we'd have to sell at a loss. People have families to think of, too."

Leslie tried to smile. "There must be some way."

"We've asked the legislature for help," Karen continued. "But they're caught short, too. Inflation has made a real mess of things. The ordinary Montanan is super conscious of his historical heritage and eager to preserve it, but the odds are against him now."

Two tables away Rick Donovan leaned forward and covered his blond playmate's hand with his own strong brown one. Leslie felt the blood rushing to her cheeks. She could not avoid seeing his every action. Perhaps she should have accepted Paul's offer to change chairs, but she did not want that insufferable man to think he could intimidate her. "There must be something we can do."

"The masquerade was a big success," Karen said.

"We've considered giving a play—all volunteers, of course. Or having an auction. Maybe both."

"They both sound like good ideas," Leslie said, devoting herself to her salad, which had just arrived. Before they had finished that, the quiche that Karen had ordered was served. Leslie tried to concentrate on the delicious combination of eggs, cheese, onions, and spinach that the waiter put before her.

Once, looking up to tell Karen how good it was, she met the eyes of Rick Donovan. Even from two tables away she could see the anger in those eyes. Defiantly she kept her head up and gave him back glance for glance. She had not done anything wrong, and she did not intend to cower in a corner like some timid little mouse.

After a moment, Paul spoke to her and she let her gaze move to him. "Are you sure he isn't bothering you, Les?"

"I'm quite sure," she said firmly. "The man's paranoid. That's hardly my fault."

Either Rick Donovan could read lips, or her voice had risen and carried to his table, for the handsome face was contorted by a fierce frown. Though she did not look at him directly, she was still aware of Donovan's reaction. "Talk about something else," Leslie said. "Something pleasant, if you can, please."

Karen smiled. "Sure, Leslie. Let me think for a minute."

Paul grinned. "While you're thinking about it, I just want to ask Les if we can dance later."

Leslie's smile was genuine. "Of course, Paul. Just let me finish my quiche." It would be good to be on the dance floor, away from Rick Donovan's burning blue eyes. Besides, she had always loved to dance, and she hadn't had many opportunities before she and Paul had been sent on assignment together. There were plenty of men eager and willing to take her dancing, but they always wanted to go further than that. Not only wanted, but expected, to get more from her than a pleasant evening on the dance floor. She had quickly grown tired of their clumsy efforts at seduction and turned down all invitations. With Paul it had been different. He had always seemed willing to respect her wishes, and so she could enjoy the music and dancing without all the hassle.

The meal was soon finished and they decided to delay ordering dessert. The music coming from the small jazz band was mellow and smooth. If only, Leslie caught herself thinking, she could reverse time and relive the previous evening. To be in Rick Donovan's arms again, to have his eyes warm and clouded with passion, to have his lips so close to hers, making every nerve in her body quiver with anticipation. What she wouldn't give for that!

"Penny?" Paul said.

Leslie shook her head. "Not worth it. Why don't you and Karen go dance? The music sounds great."

Karen smiled ruefully. "Not me. Afraid there's too much in my stomach right now. Besides, I want to repair my face, and I see a friend over there I want to speak to. Don't worry about me, Leslie. I know half the people in this place. You go dance with Paul. Get out from under Rick's eagle eye. He looks like he could really destroy you. You must have made the man plenty peeved." Leslie flushed but made no comment.

When Karen had left the table, Paul raised a quizzical eyebrow. "Shall we let them see a couple of experts in action?"

Leslie's laugh was more one of nervous relief than amusement, but she was pleased to note that it sounded good. "Yes, Paul. Let's dance. The music sounds wonderful." As she stepped into Paul's arms, she wished for a moment that she could put her head on his shoulder and be comforted. It was good to know that someone cared about her, that someone was there when she needed a friend.

Paul's arm tightened around her as they swung out onto the floor. He held her rather closer than usual, his chin against her hair. But Leslie did not protest, feeling the comfort of his arms. And, she noticed, Paul was being very careful to keep her faced away from the table where Rick Donovan sat with his blond playmate.

Leslie closed her eyes and let her head fall a little closer to Paul's shoulder. What would it be like to be cared for by a man? To have a strong shoulder to turn to for support? She swallowed a sigh. It was a situation she could not imagine. Her father had been so distant, so lost in his grief, that he had never been there when she needed him. And in school the boys had always seemed strange and childish, only interested in one thing. In fact, until she and Paul had been assigned to work together, she had had no real male friends.

There was no use thinking such thoughts and Leslie knew it. There was only one man with whom she was interested in developing an intimate relationship. And that man hated women. Oh, he played with them. Played and paid, she thought bitterly. He was just as much a user as the young women who hung around him, eager for the good things he could give them.

She must think of something else, Leslie told herself. After tonight she would never see Rick Donovan again. She and Paul had to move on. They could not stay in Helena much longer. She would have to get Karen's number so they could keep abreast of what was happening, so they would know if the Golden Star had been saved. Leslie closed her eyes and tried to concentrate. There must be something else *she* could do. Perhaps a story in the local papers. Maybe she could trade on her status as reporter for *Vacations Today.* She began to form headlines in her mind: *VACATION* REPORTER APPALLED AT LACK OF EFFORT TO SAVE THEATRE. No, that was too long. WHAT'S WRONG WITH MONTANANS, *VACATION* 'S

Reporter Asks? That was slightly better, but maybe not catching enough. Her feet followed Paul's lead automatically as her mind played with and discarded various combinations of words. She was well into the first paragraph when a muffled exclamation from Paul made her open her eyes in surprise.

"May I?" asked a deep familiar voice.

Leslie felt her legs go weak and her heart begin to pound.

"Now listen—" Paul began.

"It's all right, Paul." To her amazement, her voice was steady. "Go dance with Karen."

"Are you sure?" His tone was approaching belligerence.

"Yes, Paul. Go on."

Reluctantly he released her; then, still scowling, he made his way back to the table.

Leslie forgot him before he was out of sight. The arm that slid too competently around her pulled her quite close to the lean, hard body of Rick Donovan. "Please," she murmured, "not so close."

His smile was dangerously smooth. "Why not? You seemed to be enjoying yourself with him."

Leslie stiffened. "If you're going to be insulting, we'll just forget this dance."

"Sorry, Leslie. I don't want to be insulting."

His tone was so mild that she looked up at him in surprise. She knew immediately that it was a mistake. His eyes were crinkled in a charming smile.

"In fact, I want to apologize."

"What?" She flushed as she realized that *her* response could be heard as insulting.

However, he continued to smile. "I'm afraid I was a little hard on you today."

She could think of nothing to say; the shame of the afternoon was still with her.

"I'm afraid I jumped to the wrong conclusion," he

continued, his arm pulling her just a trifle closer. Not right against him, but near enough so that their bodies occasionally touched. It was almost more tantalizing than a continuous pressure.

"Yes, you did. And it was a tremendous jump." She pushed back against his hand, but it did no good. His arm continued to draw her inexorably toward him.

"I want to make it up to you, Leslie." His voice was warm against her ear, and she resisted an impulse to lean toward him.

"I . . . don't understand."

"We lost tonight. I ruined it. But we've got tomorrow and Sunday. Come up to Whitefish with me."

"But—we've got work to do. Paul—" She noticed the tightening of his jaw, and the short pause before he spoke.

"You're a grown woman, Leslie. You don't have to listen to him. Do you?" The vivid blue eyes looked down into hers.

"Of course not. But—"

"Spend the weekend with me, Leslie." The hand on the small of her back drew her closer, and a tremor shivered through Leslie's body. "I promise you can talk about the Golden Star. All you want. And I'll listen. Maybe you can persuade me to change my mind?"

She looked at him in surprise. "Are you serious?"

"Of course." He bent his head, and his lips brushed hers in a momentary, fleeting kiss. "Come on, Leslie. I want you. And I know you want me."

She was about to deny it. After that afternoon she had to preserve some dignity.

But he forestalled her. "It's no use, Leslie. Your eyes give you away."

She dropped her gaze quickly. He was probably right. The nearness of his body was working on hers, conjuring up memories of the night before. She wanted to go with him. That was clear. Still, she did not entirely trust him.

He could change so quickly—from smiling charmer to tyrannical villain.

"But why? You said no talk. Just bring a better offer."

"That was before I saw you." His voice was husky with desire, his breath warm against her ear.

"I have no money," she said, deliberately misunderstanding him. "I'm just a poor writer."

"I know all about you, Leslie." His eyes gleamed in the dim light. "Don't play games with me. This is a straight, aboveboard offer. We'll drive up to Whitefish in the morning. I have a cabin there. We'll swim, sail. Make love." His lips grazed her forehead. "Then Sunday night I'll bring you back. And the whole time you can do your darndest to convince me about the Star."

"I—" Leslie's feet followed his automatically as they moved around the floor. "I don't know what to say."

"Say yes. Come on, Leslie. Forget this afternoon. I told you I was sorry. Let's go back to last night. You were ready to go with the Bandit."

"I know." She tried to withdraw her gaze from his, but found it impossible.

"Please say yes, Leslie. Please." His voice, low and husky, seemed to vibrate through her body.

"All—right."

In an instant he had pulled her body close against his, his rock-hard arm molding her against him. She did not protest as his chin settled against her hair. Through her thin blouse she felt the heat of his body, and she welcomed the feel of it.

"You'll see, Leslie," he whispered. "We'll have a great time. You'll love the cabin. There's a gorgeous fireplace. And a private beach. Be sure to bring your suit."

"I will."

For some minutes they danced in silence, content in their own thoughts. Then as the music ended, he said, "I'll pick you up at seven in the morning. The Sands, right?"

71

"No." Leslie found a lump in her throat. "I'm at the Whispering Waves."

For a fraction of a second she thought he would lash out at her as he had that afternoon. But then the hard look left his eyes. "Right. The Whispering Waves. At seven. Don't disappoint me, Leslie. I'm counting on you."

"I'll be ready," she said. He looked at her for one more moment, his eyes opaque and unrevealing, and then he was gone, striding purposefully across the floor toward the table where Estelle Lamprey was waiting.

Leslie made her way back to where her friends waited.

Paul jumped up to seat her. "I'd like to punch that guy right in the nose," he growled.

Karen shook her head. "Come on, Paul. Violence never solved anything."

"I don't care," Paul grumbled. "He thinks he can push everyone around. What did he want, anyway?"

"Just to talk," Leslie said, trying to keep her voice calm. Later she would figure out what to tell Paul.

"Well," Karen said, "this is a surprise. I thought Rick Donovan had written you off."

"So did I." Leslie reached for her bag. "Excuse me for a minute. My makeup needs repair."

She did not glance toward the other table as she rose and made her way to the powder room. Once safely inside its sanctuary, she dropped into a chair. Could she trust Rick Donovan? This afternoon he had seemed so harsh, so inhuman. But tonight he had been different—the charming man who had so attracted her at the masquerade.

Well, it was already decided. She meant to go with him, and maybe she could persuade him to save the Star. It was worth the chance.

The door opened to admit Karen. "There's no sense in hiding out in here," she said cheerfully. "Rick has left. And Estelle seemed very upset."

"I wasn't hiding out."

Karen shook her head. "What did he say to you, Leslie?"

"Nothing important." She tried to keep calm.

"Sorry, Leslie. Your face gives you away. Whatever he said was pretty potent. Let me guess. He wants to see you again."

"How did you know?"

Leslie stopped as Karen smiled. "So. I was right."

"After the big row we had this afternoon, I can't understand it. He was so charming again."

"Be careful, Leslie." Karen smiled sadly. "Rick doesn't think emotions are important. He only considers physical feelings."

"I–I don't know what to do."

"I'd stay away from him, if I were you. You're outclassed, Leslie. Any decent woman is. The only ones who come away from Rick intact are the takers. And sometimes even they get hurt. He *is* a terribly attractive man."

"I know." The words were heartfelt and very revealing. As soon as Karen's eyes narrowed, Leslie wished she could recall them.

"Listen, Leslie, you aren't falling in love with the man?"

"Of course not." Leslie wished her tone was more convincing. "It was merely a physical attraction."

"Good." Karen sighed in relief. "I wouldn't want you to be hurt. I'm not sure Rick knows how to love anymore. He only knows how to take love, not to give it."

"You really cared about him, didn't you?" Leslie could not help asking the obvious question.

Karen nodded. "Yes, I did. And it took me a while to get over it, but I have. I'm not the playgirl type." She looked at Leslie curiously. "I can't believe you are either."

Leslie shook her head. "I've never—I don't know what happened to me that night. I didn't feel like the same person. Maybe it was the costume. And I'd been reading Maggie's diary."

"Maggie was your great-grandmother?"

Leslie nodded.

Karen's face grew wistful. "I know how you feel and what you want, Leslie." There was a short silence, then she shook herself slightly and patted at her hair. "I was married once and someday I'll marry again—and for love." She stood and slowly walked to the door. "And now we'd better get back to the table before Paul comes looking for us."

As Leslie followed her new friend back into the dining room, she felt a sense of relief. It helped to know that someone understood. But that didn't change what she would do tomorrow.

CHAPTER 5

The next morning Leslie sat waiting in the lobby of the Whispering Waves motel. She had packed her swimsuit, some casual clothes, and at the last minute, the green dress. She could hardly believe that she was really doing this. But it was high time she had some experience. She did not intend to make Maggie's mistake: she did not intend to fall in love. But there was no reason she could not experience passion. It was not as though she would be hurting anyone. Rick Donovan could not be hurt. It was simply a case of mutual using. And who knew? Perhaps she could persuade him to spare the Star.

Through the plate glass windows that fronted the lobby she watched the silver-gray Mercedes glide to a stop. Her heart skipped a beat as Rick climbed from the front seat and entered the lobby. His light-blue slacks and matching shirt opened almost to the waist set off his lean figure.

His eyes lighted up at the sight of her. "Leslie." Then they moved over her pale peach slacks and jersey. "That color certainly becomes you."

"Thank you." She got to her feet as he hefted the suit-case.

"Didn't forget your suit, did you?"

Leslie shook her head. "No, I love the water. And the sun."

He grinned, a strangely boyish grin that made him look years younger. "Well, Whitefish has plenty of both."

As she followed him out of the lobby Leslie was very conscious of the stares of curious onlookers. She tried to keep from flushing. After all, her life was nobody's business but her own.

He put her suitcase in the back and helped her into the front seat. Leslie smiled. "Such service."

Grinning, he slid into the driver's seat. "The Donovans always travel high-class. It's part of our style."

Leslie nodded and tried to smile, but Maggie's words were echoing in her heart. "The wicked gold is ruining Mick. It's always the best o' this and the best o' that now."

"Why the sad look?" Rick asked as the Mercedes purred into life.

Leslie smiled. "Nothing important. Just a sad memory."

"I hope our weekend hasn't caused you any problems," he said, a curious tone in his voice.

"No, no problems." She hoped he would not press her. She was rather ashamed of sneaking out on Paul. But she found their confrontations increasingly difficult. And it *was* her life. So, rather than telling him the truth last night, she had allowed him to suggest an eight o'clock breakfast and then this morning left him a note at the desk. She had kept close to the truth without telling him all of it. Whether he read between the lines and surmised that she was "getting away" *with* someone she could not tell. She would deal with that when she returned.

"You didn't tell him you were going with me." It was a statement not a question. But his voice was not mocking.

"No, I didn't."

"And you don't want to discuss it."

Leslie turned to him, a slight smile on her lips. "You're right again. I don't."

He shook his head. "I'll respect your wishes, Leslie. But I do think you're making a mistake. The man acts like he owns you."

Leslie seemed to hear a faint question in the words. "But he doesn't," she hastened to add.

"Then let him know that clearly and plainly. You're not a child." He grinned wickedly. "Don't let him play Daddy."

"That isn't what—" Leslie stopped suddenly. "I thought we weren't going to discuss it."

"All right, we won't. Have you ever sailed?"

She shook her head. "No, but it looks like fun."

"It is." His eyes slid over her speculatively. "The whole weekend is going to be fun."

"Have you had the cabin long?" Leslie asked, searching for a safe topic of conversation, since sailing did not seem to be one.

His eyes told her he recognized what she was doing, but he made no comment on it. "I built it—let's see—about five years ago."

"*You* built it?" She could not keep the surprise out of her voice.

"Yes, Leslie. I built it. Myself." He looked down at his lean brown hands, effortlessly gripping the wheel. "With my own hands. It was a very interesting experience." He grinned at her. "I'm a man of many parts, my dear. I build my own cabin, sail my own boat, pilot my own plane." His eyes rested on her warmly. "And pick my own playmates. I made a particularly good choice this time, I think."

She did not answer him, turning her head quickly to admire the passing scenery. What would he say when he discovered that he was her first? If he laughed at her, it would be unbearable. He would certainly not be expecting to find her a virgin. She could be sure of that.

"Penny for your thoughts," he said, his hand resting momentarily on her knee.

"I–I was just thinking what a state of contrasts Montana is," she improvised, hoping he would not guess what

77

she was doing. "The eastern part is flat and grassy. And this part is wooded and hilly."

Rick nodded. "I thought your article was just about Helena."

"It is." Leslie clasped her hands nervously.

"Then why were you in the eastern part of the state?"

"I wasn't. I–I just *like* Montana. I've read a lot about it."

"I see."

She hoped he wouldn't pursue the subject. "Tell me, what does Donovan and Donovan do besides sell buildings?"

His eyes narrowed, and she wondered if she had hit a nerve. "We handle all kinds of real estate. Among other things. You don't want to hear about it. It's deadly boring." His hand crossed her cheek in a fleeting caress. "*You* tell me, Leslie, why this infatuation with old buildings."

"I . . ." She paused. She couldn't tell him about Maggie and Mick. He might think she had some ulterior motive. But surely she could mention the diary. "It isn't *just* old buildings," she replied. "I *like* old buildings. They're fascinating. But Helena's are even more so. And the Star most of all."

"But why?" His eyes held hers for a moment before they swung back to the road.

"You remember how I told you my name was Maggie Callahan?"

He nodded.

"Well, I didn't just grab that name out of thin air. Maggie was my great-grandmother. She came here from New York's Irish tenements. And she loved it here."

"And the Golden Star?"

"Maggie danced there."

"She was a dancer?"

She saw the quick gleam in his eye and rushed to answer it. "Maggie wasn't . . . loose."

Rick's grin was disbelieving. "Then she must have been very unusual. From what I understand those girls could all be had. It was their second profession, so to speak."

Leslie's irritation made her voice sharp. "Not Maggie."

Rick looked surprised. "How do you know?"

"I have Maggie's diary. Her private personal diary that she never meant for anyone to see. Maggie saved herself for the man she loved." Even to Leslie the words sounded ridiculously old-fashioned.

Rick laughed outright.

"I know it sounds funny," she said. "But it's true. Maggie was a devout Catholic."

"But she gave herself to the man she loved," he repeated.

"Yes. They meant to get married." Leslie began to wish she had not mentioned the diary.

"Meant to." Rick gave her a strange look. "I bet they didn't."

"You're right," Leslie said softly. "They didn't."

"It's just as well," he replied cynically. "Marriage is never a good deal. Better to be a free agent. So what happened to Maggie and her lover?"

"He struck it rich and decided he was too good for her." Leslie watched him closely, but he didn't seem to relate to the story personally.

"He married someone else, huh?"

"Yes. And then he asked Maggie to continue as his mistress."

"A man after my own heart," Donovan said with a harsh laugh. "But I don't imagine your pure Maggie could handle it."

Leslie swallowed over the sudden lump in her throat, remembering the words that told of Maggie's pain. "She believed in the sanctity of marriage. Her man had to be all hers."

He shook his head. "So she lost him altogether. What sense was there in that?"

Leslie shrugged. "I don't know. But it made sense to Maggie. She loved him so much, she wouldn't be party to such a sin." She flinched at the word—but it was Maggie's word. "The day he married his rich heiress from the East Maggie went back to New York."

"And then to Cleveland."

"How did you know that?"

"You're from Cleveland," he said, his voice nonchalant.

For a second Leslie faced the suspicion that he had had her investigated. He had certainly known all about *Vacations Today*. But surely he did not investigate every woman he slept with. The thought was ridiculous. She was getting almost as paranoid as he, she thought.

"So you want to save the theatre that Maggie danced in?"

"Yes, I do. It's a beautiful old place. It should be preserved. Surely you can see that."

"The motel they want to put there will bring income to its owners and to the city," he pointed out. "The theatre can't do that."

"It could be used for some kind of performances. Or as a museum," Leslie insisted. "And, anyway, must money always be your measure?" She was unable to keep the bitterness out of her voice.

He glanced at her, his face showing the vestiges of surprise. "It's the measure of the world, Leslie. You'd better recognize that. It's silly to disregard such things."

"I don't care." Leslie heard the note of defiance in her voice and tried to temper it. "Money isn't everything. What about love?"

Rick's laugh wasn't pleasant to hear. "You must be kidding. Love? That's a dream for dumb teenagers. Now lust . . ." The teeth beneath the bushy black mustache gleamed as he smiled at her. "Lust is a different story. But we know all about that, don't we, Leslie?"

She nodded, her heart beginning to thump. "I suppose so." There was silence for a few moments. Then the words came out before she could stop them. "Don't you want children?"

Something strange flickered in his eyes for a moment, but his voice was even as he answered. "Children? I suppose I'll get around to it someday. There's plenty of time."

Something told Leslie that his indifference was feigned. "But won't you want to love their mother?"

He shrugged. "As long as she's suitable, that'll be enough."

"Suitable?" She choked on the word. "Suitable! You sound like a–a horsebreeder."

"Maybe I do." His voice remained even. "It doesn't really matter. One thing I know for sure. I'll never marry for love." He looked at her sharply. "Don't tell me *you* intend to marry?"

She shook her head. "I haven't given it much thought. But I suppose I'll want to. Someday."

"You want children?" he asked.

"I–I don't know." Her mind gave her a sudden picture of a baby with curly black hair and vivid blue eyes—Rick Donovan's baby. She managed a shaky little laugh. It sounded a trifle brittle, but it helped to mask her anxiety. "I wouldn't want to have children unless I loved their father. And unless he loved me." Her voice broke. "And them."

There was a moment's silence before Rick Donovan spoke. "Tell me about your family, Leslie."

She tried to smile. "There isn't much to tell."

"Tell me what there is." His voice was strangely gentle.

"My mother died when I was ten." Leslie kept her voice even. "Before that I remember lots of good times, laughing-together times. After that . . ." She paused for a moment. "My father was a college professor. He loved my mother dearly."

"And not you." His tone was so kind that Leslie nodded before she realized what she was doing.

"No! I mean, of course, he loved me." She felt the hot rush of tears to her eyes.

"Leslie, it's not your fault."

She swallowed over the lump in her throat. "It wasn't his fault either. Part of him died when she did. All he had left were his books."

"And you were lonely."

She nodded. "Yes, I couldn't help it. But how did you know so much?"

"It takes one to know one."

The pain in his voice registered for her, and she thought of those moments on the hill above Helena when he had spoken of the lights in the homes below. "What do you mean?"

"I was an only child, too. Only my father didn't love my mother. He just loved his business. And my mother loved her charitable activities." He gave her a quick look. "Among them a handful of preservation societies."

"Oh." The sound fell into the sudden silence. "I guess that explains your distaste for history."

"I suppose it does. I wanted a mother. Not a bunch of old buildings. Oh, I had the cook and the housekeeper, but they were changed every year or two. I did as I pleased. A life of complete freedom. I suppose most kids would like that."

Leslie did not know how to answer him. This at least explained the fact that he was so arrogant and overbearing. But it gave her a very different view of him than she had had before. He had been badly hurt as a child. She could see that. Still, he needn't have turned out as he had.

She had been lonely and uncared for. But, of course, she had had to think about her future. Rick Donovan had had

82

no such problem. There had always been plenty of money for him. Plenty of money and plenty of freedom to spend it. That had been the curse of Rick Donovan's life. Money had ruined him just as it had ruined Maggie's Mick. And after all that freedom no wonder he had been so angry at his parents' interference when he fell in love—or thought he had.

"I don't know how we got onto this subject," he said, his voice determindedly cheerful. "We're on our way for a *fun* weekend. Remember?"

Leslie smiled. "I remember. How much longer till we get there?"

Rick consulted his watch. "Probably another hour or so. Why don't you lean back and take a little nap? You'll want to be fresh when we get there."

Obediently Leslie leaned back in the seat and closed her eyes. She did not feel sleepy, but she was aware that Rick Donovan did not want to talk. His determindedly cheerful tone had not masked the look of pain in his eyes. He was remembering things and he wanted to be left alone.

A gentle hand on her shoulder shook Leslie awake. For a moment she didn't know where she was, then she heard Rick's voice. "We're almost there," he said. "Have a nice nap?"

She raised her head and rubbed at her eyes. "Yes. The car is very comfortable."

"Good." His grin spoke volumes, and Leslie felt her skin grow flushed at the look in his eyes. "Shall we stop in a restaurant for lunch or will you trust to my cooking? I've got a trunk full of groceries."

"You can cook?" Leslie's astonishment was evident.

"I told you. I'm a man of many parts."

"I'm beginning to believe it." She answered his grin with one of her own. "I'll trust to your kitchen accomplishments."

"Good." Rick glanced at the sky. "I'm anxious to get in the water. Now, don't expect too much of me at lunchtime. Just sandwiches. But I promise you something special tonight."

Leslie laughed, a soft little sound. "I'll settle for that."

"Agreed then. Look, there it is. Whitefish Lake. One of the prettiest little lakes in the country."

"Yes." Leslie's face was a study as she surveyed the water. "How blue it is. And the sky, too." She did not notice the strange look, almost of bewilderment, with which he was regarding her.

"You'll enjoy sailing. I know you will. You *do* swim?"

Leslie grinned. "Of course. Like a fish."

"Great."

"But I've never sailed."

"It's a piece of cake. I'll teach you." As he talked Rick was guiding the car along the road that wound beside the lake. "And here we are."

"Here?" Leslie looked at a tangle of trees and wild brush. "I don't see anything."

He suddenly swung the car sideways and down a tree-lined drive. "That's the idea," he said softly. "I like my privacy."

The bushes and small trees that lined the driveway crowded close to the gravel, cutting off the view of the water. Then Rick turned another curve and came to a stop behind a cabin. Beyond it Leslie could see a stretch of sand and then the glorious blue of the water.

"Oh," she breathed. "It's absolutely beautiful."

He beamed. "Thank you. I like it. Wait till you see the fireplace in action tonight. I built it, too."

He slid out and came around to open the door for her. "I'll carry in your suitcase first. Why don't you slip into your suit while I slap together some lunch?"

"Great." Leslie followed him into the cabin. "Oh, Rick, it's just beautiful." The front wall, the one facing the lake,

84

was dominated by a great stone fireplace in its exact center. This was flanked on both sides by two large sliding glass windows that gave a breathtaking view of the lake. Leslie turned to the rest of the room. Even the furniture looked handmade, including the oversized bed that filled one corner, its great mattress hidden by a huge fur throw. Flushing, Leslie turned away from it to face the other back corner that held a miniature kitchen, complete with stove and refrigerator.

Rick set a box of groceries on the little table. "The bathroom's through there," he said. "I put your suitcase on the bed."

"Thanks." Leslie opened the case, her fingers accidentally brushing against the silky fur. Quickly she drew out her bikini and beach coat and hurried into the bathroom. It, too, was rustic, but had all the modern conveniences.

She slipped out of her clothes and into the bikini. It seemed to have shrunk since the last time she'd worn it. Worriedly she pulled at the scanty top, but it would not cover any more of her. Sighing, she pulled on the white terry beach coat and tied it around her. It was silly to be so nervous.

Before the little mirror she braided her hair and fastened it with a rubber band, before she wrapped it around her head and pinned it up with the pins she kept in her beach-coat pocket. She stared at herself in the glass. How was it that Rick Donovan wanted *her*?

"Lunch's ready," he called.

Leslie took a deep breath. "Coming." Grasping the door knob firmly, she stepped out.

"My, that was fast," she said.

He looked up from the table. "I confess I cheated," He indicated the plastic-wrapped sandwiches. "I picked them up at the delicatessen. But dinner will be all mine. From scratch. Take your pick. They're labeled. Chicken, ham, sausage, tuna. There's pop and wine in the fridge." He grinned. "I'll just go get into my trunks. See you in a minute."

"Okay." Leslie unwrapped a chicken sandwich. To her surprise she realized that she was hungry. She opened the small refrigerator and snapped open a soft drink. It's coldness was refreshing against her hot, dry throat.

She was unwrapping a tuna sandwich, her back to the bathroom, when she heard the door open and close.

"Now it's time for some sun and water."

Leslie nodded. She did not trust herself to turn toward him, but kept on eating.

He came around her and perched on one of the stools by the table. Leslie swallowed hastily. In swim trunks he was even more attractive. His shoulders were broad, the muscles rippling under the sun-bronzed skin of his back and arms. His chest hair formed a broad black stripe down the center of his body and fine dark hair curled on his arms and legs. Leslie raised her soft drink as he grabbed a couple of sandwiches and a drink.

"Let's go on out to the beach. I can't wait."

"Okay."

He put the sandwiches into her hands. "If you'll carry these, I'll bring the rest." And he picked up a beach bag that was resting by the door.

The sun was hot on her bare feet as Leslie followed him outside. She watched as he spread the blanket, then settled beside him.

He took the sandwiches from her. "All the comforts of home, eh, Leslie?"

"Yes. You must love it here."

He grinned. "I do. But it's not *old*. Maybe I should have kept the shack that was here when I bought the land."

"Really, Rick." She glared at him in mock anger. "I don't have a fixation on all old buildings. Your cabin is just right here. A perfect fit."

86

"And maybe the conglomerate's hotel would fit Reeder's Alley."

Leslie shook her head. "It's not the same thing."

"I don't see why not. An old building is an old building."

"The Golden Star has character." She looked at him with exasperation. "It's not just any old shack."

"Any old shack can have character, too," he said, biting into a sandwich. "But never mind that. Just enjoy. Did you bring your sunglasses?"

"I left them in the cabin, in my purse."

"There're some in the beach bag. Might as well get out the suntan oil, too."

Leslie nodded. The bag held several pair of glasses. She selected ones with white rims to match her suit, wondering with a little twinge what woman had worn them last. She put the bottle of suntan oil on the blanket beside him.

"You won't get much tan with your beach coat on." His voice held a hint of amusement.

"Oh, I forgot." Leslie put down the empty soft-drink can and tugged at the coat.

"Lay it over there," he suggested. "When I'm through eating, I'll rub some oil on you. We don't want you to burn."

Leslie nodded, her throat suddenly gone dry. It was ridiculous to feel so self-conscious. In an effort to hide her nervousness she stretched out on her stomach, her head turned away from him.

The sun was warm on her back, its feel almost like a caress, and she stretched a little, welcoming the feel of it. She wanted to concentrate on remembering this weekend. She wanted to store up every moment for future reference.

His sandwich paper rustled as he crumpled it into a ball, and her muscles tensed as he said, "And now to work."

The sun was warm on her body, but his hands were warmer still. They smoothed the oil over her in long leisurely strokes. And while they smoothed, gently, tenderly, they also caressed. She felt longing rise inside her as he took his time, touching every exposed part of her body, anointing it liberally with oil.

"Now the front. Roll over."

She felt a moment of hesitation.

"Come on, my girl. Roll over."

Leslie obeyed. The dark glasses hid her eyes, but she couldn't control the slight quiver of her bottom lip. She felt completely exposed as his hands moved softly over her, first her arms and shoulders, including the white flesh above her bikini top, then her legs and feet, every touch a caress. And then his hands lingered on her bare midriff, moving up close to the wisp of material that confined her breasts and down across the tender skin of her stomach to the elastic of her bikini bottom. Leslie lay supine, but every nerve in her body tingled from his touch.

Finally he spoke again. "All done."

Leslie let out a small sigh and willed her muscles to relax.

A slim brown finger trailed across her bare stomach. "Turnabout is fair play," he teased.

"What?" She was so startled that she sat up.

"I said it's your turn to do me." He put the bottle in her hand, closing her fingers around it, and then flopped down on his stomach beside her.

Leslie let her eyes travel down the lean length of him, from the broad shoulders to the narrow hips and down his well-muscled legs.

"Anything wrong?" he asked, turning his head to look at her.

"No, no." She poured oil onto his back and began to spread it, the skin warm and smooth under her fingers.

"Hmmmmm," he murmured lazily. "You do that well."

Leslie stifled a nervous laugh. "Thank you, sir." She

took a long time over her task, covering every inch of his back and shoulders. Then she paused, uncertain what to do next.

"The legs," he whispered. "Don't forget the legs."

For some reason Leslie was even more embarrassed when confronted by his legs.

"Well—"

"Yes, I'm doing it." The fine hair tickled her palms as she smoothed the oil over his strong legs. They were already bronzed a deep brown by the sun. "You don't even need any suntan oil," she said when she had finished. "You're really brown already."

"I know." He turned over with a grin. "But it's so much fun to have you spread it on."

"Rick Donovan!"

His merriment was infectious, his grin that of a mischievous little boy. "You didn't do the front yet."

"You don't need it," she protested.

"Maybe not the oil." His hand reached out to touch her cheek. For a long moment their eyes held. Then he took her hand and put it on his chest. "Back to work, woman. Oil me up."

"Yes, sir."

He closed his eyes against the sun and smiled in contentment as her hand began to move on his chest. Leslie gazed with fascination at the deep brown skin and the crisp little hairs curling under her fingers, the oil on them glistening in the sunlight. She oiled his whole chest, then absently played with the hairs, smoothing them out and watching them curl up again. She noted the smooth rise and fall of his chest, the strong curves of his throat, the firm line of his chin jutting out from under the bushy black mustache. The dark glasses he wore hid his eyes, those brilliant blue eyes that could do such strange things to her. Lazily she ran a finger down the line of dark hair that

89

stretched from just below his chin down past his navel and disappeared into his white trunks.

"Hmmmmm, nice."

She looked up to find him grinning at her. Suddenly his hands went around her bare waist. "Come here, woman." And he pulled her up against him, her face level with his.

"The oil, Rick! You'll spill it!"

"Doesn't matter," he said, taking it from her hand. He removed her glasses and put them to one side, then set his own there, too. Then his arms were around her, pressing her down against him, their skins slippery with the oil.

She felt the hair on his chest pressing against her bare stomach and buried her face in his shoulder. Her cheek slid along the smooth flesh, fitting into the hollow below his chin. His hands spanned her waist and slid up her oiled back, trailing over the bare skin and sending little waves of desire through her flesh. She clung to him, the sun warm on her back, his body warm and virile beneath her.

One hand slid up her back to the exposed nape of her neck and lingered there, his fingers moving in a soft caress. "Hmmmm," Leslie allowed herself a murmur of delight.

"You're all slippery," he said, merriment in his voice.

"So are you." She had not imagined it would be like this, this element of lighthearted fun running through everything.

His hands, strong on her waist, suddenly slid her up and down his body and she felt a giggle bubbling up in her throat.

"What's it feel like?" he asked, his eyes sparkling.

"Sort of like being a done cookie," she giggled, "sliding off the cookie sheet onto the plate."

"Pretty good," he said. "But not very poetic. A writer should be able to do better than that."

"Hmmmmm, let me think. I've got it—like butter melting on pancakes."

Rick laughed, hearty laughter that shook the body beneath her own. "Food again. Don't you ever think of anything else?"

"Sometimes," she said, not telling him that the metaphor was so apt because her body *felt* like it was melting, melting into his.

He pulled her up again so that her face was even with his. "You've got suntan oil on your face," he said, brushing her cheek, those vivid blue eyes looking up into hers. "Glad you came?" he asked.

Leslie nodded. "Very glad."

For a long moment he held her gaze. Then his hand slid to her nape again, pulling her lips down against his. It was a long kiss, tender and persuasive, and she felt his growing hardness as her own desire began to rise.

Finally he turned his head a little. "Say, let a fellow breathe, will you?"

She let her head fall against his shoulder. "Sure, anything you say."

His hands moved softly, tracing lines up and down her back. Leslie sighed in contentment, strangely at peace in spite of her desire.

Suddenly he rolled her over on her back, his body pressing her into the blanket. Slowly he lifted himself and smiled down at her. "How about a swim?"

She wanted to pull him down against her, to hook her arms around his neck and not let him go, but she smiled instead. "Sounds great."

In one quick motion he got to his feet and extended his hand to pull her up. Then they went toward the water's edge, arms around each other's waists.

"Is it usually cold?" Leslie asked.

"Nah. It's warm as—" He grinned. "Just try it."

"I will!" Leslie dropped her arm from his waist. "Race you."

She took off down the beach, her bare feet throwing up the sand behind her. As she hit the water she heard an echoing splash beside her. The lake was cold, but not terribly so, and relishing the feel of it against her overheated skin, she struck out toward the stationary raft bobbing some distance away.

Minutes later she reached the raft. As her hands grasped its edge Rick leaned over her. "What kept you?" he grinned. "I've been here for hours."

"I'm a little rusty. Haven't had much time for swimming lately."

"Too bad. Looks like you really needed this rest."

"I did." She shook the water from her face, her eyes going to the glistening drops dripping from his heaving chest, running down the muscles of his arms. "You're not fooling me. You just got here yourself!"

He pulled her up onto the raft beside him. "It's that writer's sense of observation," he teased, his eyes twinkling. His arm went around her bare shoulders and a flush of warmth spread over her as he pressed her close against his side. "Where did you go on your last vacation?" he asked conversationally.

"I don't remember." She was sorry as soon as the words left her mouth. It would have been far simpler to lie.

"You don't remember?" The blue eyes were serious now.

"I–I've been busy." It was a lame excuse, and she knew it.

"If you're that busy, when do you have time to play?"

"I manage." She snuggled closer, enjoying the feel of his body, trying to put down the nagging fear of what he would say when he learned of her virginity.

His expression was puzzled. "What was your last article about?"

"Hale Farm in Akron."

"You have a thing about old buildings."

She smiled. "I guess so." She looked out across the

brilliant blue water. "They just fascinate me. I'm a kind of history buff."

Rick grimaced. "History. Yuck." Then his expression grew thoughtful. "History, huh? Your father's field."

Leslie turned to him in surprise. "My father taught medieval history. That has nothing to do with what I like."

"History is history," he said calmly.

"You don't understand. I like to read about the past, especially Montana's past, because of Maggie. It's the years when she was alive that I like best to read about. It makes her more real to me somehow."

"Real?" Rick's voice held a note of surprise.

Leslie continued to look out over the water, her voice soft. "I told you, I found the diary after Mother died." She felt Rick's fingers tighten sympathetically on her shoulder. "Dad couldn't cope. Maybe I reminded him of Mom. I don't know, but he just wasn't there. And the diary was; Maggie was." She paused, searching for words to make him understand. "I needed someone. Maggie was all I had."

For some moments there was silence, no sound but the soft lapping of waves against the raft.

Then Rick spoke. "I suppose in a way you were lucky. You had *someone.*"

She heard the hurt in his voice, but did not turn her head to look at him, only letting her arm steal out to encircle his waist. They sat for some minutes in companionable silence.

Then suddenly he turned and pulled her to him. This kiss was not like the others; there was something of comfort in it. Comfort and warm affection. "Beat you back to shore," he challenged, leaping to his feet and hitting the water in one swift motion.

Leslie followed, but in spite of all her efforts could not

catch up with him. He was grinning as she came up the beach behind him. "Beat you again."

"That's not fair," she cried. "You had a head start."

He nodded, his eyes twinkling. "I always take all the advantages I can get."

Leslie nodded, her mouth still curved in a smile, but she felt an inward chill. All the advantages, he had said. And it was true. This whole thing was new to her, new, and perhaps much more dangerous than she had imagined.

Rick grabbed her hand. "Come on, time for a little sailing lesson before that gourmet dinner I promised you."

"Okay." Leslie allowed him to lead her toward the boat house.

"Socks and sneakers in the locker over there," he said, opening another locker and pulling out a disreputable pair of sneakers.

Leslie selected a pair of the fresh white socks and some sneakers, conveniently labeled by size. "You're certainly well prepared." She could not resist saying it.

He shrugged. "I get a lot of company out here." He made a face. "Sometimes more than I want. And most of them don't bring the right stuff." He pushed the button that opened the door and climbed into the boat.

"It looks very small," Leslie said, finishing with a shoe-string.

"It's an eighteen-footer. Plenty big enough for this lake. Come aboard." He extended a hand and she took it, stepping down into the cockpit.

"Sit there," he pointed. "I'll just use the auxiliary motor to ease us out of here. We'll put the sail up later."

"Right, boss."

"The correct word is captain," he said with another grin.

"Aye, aye, Captain."

As the little boat began to move out into the lake Leslie leaned back against the seat. The boat was expensive; she, who knew very little about boats, knew that. "You didn't build this, did you?"

He chuckled. "No, Leslie. That would have taken too long." He looked over the boat with appreciation. "Pretty little thing, isn't she?"

"Yes." Leslie smiled. "Do men always look at their boats like that?" she asked.

"How?"

"Almost as if you were looking at a woman. With–with tenderness, almost love in your eyes." She saw the tightening of his jaw at the word love, and wondered if she had unleashed a demon in him.

He frowned slightly. "I'd much rather love a boat than a woman. It's much more sensible."

She could not resist asking. "Why?"

His smile wasn't pleasant. "A boat responds to the treatment it gets."

"Just like a woman does." Leslie's voice held challenge.

He shook his head. "Not so, Leslie baby. Now, take this boat. She responds to me. And I know her responses will always be the same under the same conditions. But a woman . . ." He frowned. "Women are unpredictable. You never can tell about them."

Leslie bit back a sharp reply. With his background there was little point in trying to change his mind. And she did not want to spoil the weekend by making him really angry. "Has the boat a name?"

Rick nodded. "Of course. Don't all boats?"

Leslie smiled. "What is its name? I suppose you named it after an old flame."

He grinned as he shook his head. "Not so. I've already mentioned her name."

"No, you haven't."

"Yes, I have."

"Come on, Rick. Don't tease me."

"I'm not. I did mention her name. Her name is She."

"She?"

He nodded. "She."

"The Eternal Feminine," Leslie replied. "How very appropriate."

"I thought so." His grin was warm, and his eyes lingered on her partially exposed body. "Of course, if I'd known you then, I might have named her the Leslie."

Her heart skipped a beat, but her smile did not betray it. "I really think She is better. But I'm surprised at your reading H. Rider Haggard."

"Why? I read a lot when I was young. We had a big library full of older works." His statement was offhand, but his tone betrayed the loneliness she had heard before.

"Me, too, except I had to use the university library."

He smiled at her as he got to his feet, his hands moving busily as he hoisted the white sail. "And now it's time for Sailing Lesson Number One."

CHAPTER 6

The sun was low on the horizon when Rick eased the sailboat back into the boat house. Leslie, sitting quietly in the cockpit, looked out over the lake, now mirroring the sky's myriad colors.

"We get some fantastic sunsets out here," he said. "But there are even better ones on the plains. I've driven into a sunset for two hours straight."

Leslie sighed in contentment. The afternoon had been exhilarating. She had always loved the out-of-doors, and especially the water. Rick's explanations had been clear and brief, and although she did not yet feel herself a sailor, she did think she had some understanding of the thing.

Rick helped her from the boat, smiled warmly, and dropped a kiss on her forehead. "That was great. I'll make a sailor of you yet."

Leslie's heart leaped at the promise of a future that his words held, but she immediately reminded herself that for her and Rick Donovan there *was* no future. She had better remember that.

"Now here's the plan," he said as they replaced the sneakers and returned to the beach. "It'll take me about half an hour or so to get cleaned up. You can sit out here and admire Montana. Then I'll call you and you can bathe and change while I fix dinner. Agreed?"

Leslie nodded. "Agreed."

For a moment Leslie stood watching him stride toward

the cabin, admiring the swing of those lean hips, the play of muscles under the bronzed skin. Then she dropped down on the blanket, still warm from the afternoon sun. Absently she drew her legs up under her chin.

The sunset was a spectacular one, the blue of the sky shot through with rust, orange, gold, and rose. But Leslie did not really see it, for the moment that had been on her mind all day would soon be arriving. And how would she respond? She knew that she wanted Rick, as he wanted her. But she had so little firsthand knowledge, and when he discovered that she was not a "fun" girl, that he was her first, would he be pleased or angry?

It was impossible to tell.

In an effort to ease her mind she started recalling the events of the day. He had been very charming, listening to her with polite attention, even drawing her out. An act she would never have thought possible of the harsh arrogant bully of the previous afternoon. And while they'd been sailing, he'd been unfailingly patient with her, repeating again and again until she could grasp the idea.

Leslie shivered and clasped her arms around her pulled-up knees. But no matter where they were or what they had been doing, she had been continually aware of the underlying current of sexual tension growing between them. His brief caresses, the accidental contacts of their bodies, even the sight of his bronzed flesh, all combined to build within her an increasing desire. And soon he would satisfy it.

And then, thought Leslie, then she would know what it was to be a woman in the fullest sense. She would know desire and passion. One of Maggie's passages about the splendor of love came to her mind. But that was inappropriate, she told herself firmly, disregarding a little inward shiver, because she, Leslie Jordan, knew exactly what she was doing, and love played no part in it at all. Not because like Rick she did not believe in it, but because she was too wise to allow herself that painful ecstasy. There would be this weekend, and that was all. She had known that clearly from the beginning. And in spite of the fun-filled afternoon and the moments of disclosure and tenderness they had shared, she knew it still.

"Your turn." Rick's voice echoed through the stillness.

"Coming." Leslie cast one last unseeing look at the dying sun and turned toward the cabin.

He had opened one of the sliding glass doors that faced the beach, and she slipped in through it, setting the blanket and beach bag on the floor. He was wearing black slacks and his chest and feet were bare, his dark hair still glistening from the water. "Take your time," he said. "I'll just be getting dinner." His eyes slid over her. "I hope you're going to wear that green thing I saw sticking out of your case."

With a start Leslie realized that she had left her bag open. She smiled. "Aye, aye, Captain." Grabbing up her dress and toilet articles, she made her way to the bathroom.

Did he know, she wondered, how devastatingly male he looked like that? The answer came swiftly. Of course he did. And probably he knew exactly how she would respond to this day of tantalization. With a smile Leslie began to fill the tub with tepid water. When she came out wearing that green dress, she would do her own share of tantalizing.

Before stepping into the tub she undid her hair and shampooed it in the sink, toweling it dry and pinning the mass of damp curls to the crown of her head. Then she lay back in the water, letting it wash away the sand and salt, trying to ease some of the tension within her.

But relaxation would not come, and it wasn't long before Leslie was toweling dry. Self-consciously she traced the shape of her mouth with a light lipstick. Her complexion seemed to have acquired a golden glow from her hours in the sun, and her eyes stared back at her from the mirror with a mixed look of anxiety and excitement.

With a little shiver she slid into the green dress, adjusting the folds of the shoulders. The mirror showed her the soft valley between her breasts and Leslie took a deep breath. She would have to face him. The sooner the better.

He was busy with the salad, his back to her, as Leslie moved noiselessly across the room on bare feet. "That looks good," she said, trying to mask her nervousness.

He set down the knife he was holding and turned to her. For a long minute his eyes rested on her body, and waves of embarrassment rose over her. "Wow!" His voice was low and husky. "Now that's a gown. I bet you've driven dozens of guys crazy with that one."

Leslie, her eyes on his chest, answered without thinking. "No, it's new."

"Bought it for me, huh?" His eyes gleamed. "Well, it's a great success."

"Thank you. I'm glad you like it." She hardly knew what she was saying. His eyes were hot on her, so hot, she thought she could actually feel their touch.

"Come here, baby."

Leslie hesitated for only a moment before she moved into his open arms. His lips were warm against her ear. "If you're not careful," he whispered. "You won't get any dinner." And then his mouth sought hers. The kiss, though short, left her shaken. "Sit over there," he said as he put her from him. "I have the salad about ready. The wine is waiting. And in a minute you can watch me cook the steaks. Okay?"

"Okay." She moved across the room to the pile of cushions he had indicated. Banked coals glowed in the stone fireplace and Leslie inched closer, grateful for their warmth. The breeze coming through the open window was cool. On the raised hearth the wine sat in an ice bucket, two long-stemmed glasses gleaming beside it. A basket held crusty slices of bread, already buttered, and plates and silver were waiting.

Rick came toward her, carrying two steaks, the salad, and some utensils. "I like to cook them over the fire," he said, dropping down beside her. "Do you like your salad first or with the steak?"

Leslie fought down the desire to reach out and caress the brown shoulder so close to her. "With it," she replied.

Rick nodded. "Me, too. Now watch, this is my own invention." With the long fork he held he pulled a steel rack from the side of the fireplace. "It's built to swivel out," he explained as it swung out over the coals at just the right height to broil the steaks.

"Ingenious," said Leslie, watching him lay out the steaks above the glowing coals.

He cast her a quick glance. "I thought so." He grinned. "Especially as steak is one of my specialties."

She glanced around the comfortable room. "You've certainly got good living down pat," she remarked absently and was dismayed to hear a note of disapproval in her voice.

But if he heard it, he disregarded it, for he turned to her with genuine amusement. "Practice makes perfect, my dear. And I'm nearly perfect."

His brash grin invited a brash reply, and she banished the disconcerting picture of him entertaining other women here in this romantic firelit room. "I have yet to make a judgment on that," she responded, matching his grin with one of her own.

"It won't be long now, doll." His eyes went frankly to the front of her gown before they lifted to her face. "Pour us a little wine. I have to watch these steaks. By the way, how do you like yours?"

"Well done," she said as she reached for the wine bottle.

"Well done?" His voice was teasing. "You're going to ruin a good steak by having it well done."

101

Her hand was firm as she filled the glasses. "Well done," she repeated. "If it's red, I can't eat it. I promise," she added, extending him a glass and raising her eyes to his, "I promise not to complain if it's tough."

His fingers brushed hers as he took the glass, and she felt a quick shiver of excitement. "Very well, if you insist." He shook his head dolefully. "How about dishing out the salad? It's already tossed."

Leslie was glad to be able to busy herself with something. Her fingers ached to touch him, and she yearned for the feel of his body against hers.

She set the plates side by side on the hearth, a bowl of salad by each, and moved a cushion for him to sit on. Then she sipped at her wine. It was slightly sweet to the taste, and it glowed a rosy pink in the firelight. She looked to where the glowing embers cast fitful shadows over his dark skin, making him faintly mysterious. The silence in the room grew.

"I wish I were a painter," he said suddenly, startling her.

"Why?"

"So I could paint you sitting there." His eyes reflected the glowing coals. "You've no idea how beautiful you look with the firelight playing over you." His smile left her slightly breathless. "If I weren't absolutely famished from this afternoon, I'd chuck these prime steaks into the coals and have you right this minute. That look in your eyes is enough to drive a man mad."

Leslie dropped her eyes in confusion. They could very well be giving her away, speaking to him of the rising desire that was enveloping her.

"It won't be long now," he said, merriment lacing his voice so that she looked up at him in surprise. "Till the steaks are done, of course."

"Of course." Leslie replied, laughter bubbling to the surface. She had not imagined it would be like this, this laughter and friendly camaraderie. Moments of dark passion could be disregarded as temporary aberration, or so she believed. But how was she to wipe from her memory these scenes of friendly raillery, this feeling that was sometimes so strong of having always known the dark, handsome man who so soberly watched the broiling steaks?

"Plates," he said and obediently she passed them to him, watching while he took the steaks from over the coals. "Salt, pepper, steak sauce," he said, indicating the tray that held them. Then he passed her his plate and settled down beside her. "Dig in."

She had not been aware of hunger, but she found herself with a huge appetite, and the steak, which she gratefully noted showed no tinge of red, soon vanished, along with salad and several slices of the delicious crusty bread.

"Ahhhh!" said Rick, pushing away his empty plate and refilling the wine glasses. "Fit for a king."

Leslie nodded, her hand slightly unsteady as she raised her glass. How would he do it? she asked herself. Would he romance her first, or would he calmly suggest that they adjourn to the big bed, darkly mysterious beyond the circle of firelight?

"Sit still," he said, putting more wood on the fire before gathering the dirty dishes. "I'll be right back."

Obediently Leslie remained in her place, the wineglass cradled between long narrow fingers, her eyes unseeing on the flames. And then he was back, carrying the great fur throw from the bed. He spread it there before the fire. "Throw me the cushions," he said and she complied, setting down her glass to toss him each cushion. He built them into a pyramid to support their backs and leaned against them, his feet stretched toward the fire now blazing brightly. "Bring the wine over here, doll."

Leslie nodded. She was seated now on the edge of the raised hearth, and she picked up the ice bucket and leaned toward him. As he took it from her outstretched hands, his eyes rested appreciatively on the front of her gown, and Leslie flushed as she stood up and took the wineglasses.

He reached up for them both, putting them off to one side. Then he extended his hand for hers and pulled her down beside him. The fur was soft and luxuriant under her bare feet, and she felt her dress soft against her legs as he pulled her against him. For long moments she rested there in the circle of his arm, her cheek against the hard muscle of his upper arm, her face in the hollow of his throat. One hand rested against the dark matted hair of his chest and under her fingers she felt the steady beating of his heart. One of her breasts was crushed against his side, the other, having half-escaped from the gown, also rested against his bare chest. It was a magic moment, and Leslie tried to imprint in her mind all the impressions her much-assailed senses were trying to report to her.

The hand that held her close to him moved up over the bare skin of her back in a teasing caress and then stopped to cradle the nape of her neck. Heat began to suffuse her face as his other hand moved softly across her bare arm to cup her chin and raise her face to his. "Hello, lovely lady." His voice was low, a caress in itself.

"Hello." The word was a mere whisper as she stared fascinated at the vivid blue eyes so close to her own.

And then, slowly but inexorably, he increased the pressure on her neck, bringing her lips to his.

Leslie expected a hot fumbling passion, the kind that had flared between them so suddenly on that first night. And there was passion here. But it was different somehow. His lips sought hers; tenderly, gently, almost tentatively, they explored her mouth. And when her own parted under them it was with similar tenderness that his tongue mingled with hers.

His fingers moved upward, removing the pins that held her hair, and it fell to her bare shoulders in an auburn cloud. He twisted a strand of it around his finger, his

104

mouth still close to hers. "Spun copper," he whispered, his other hand spreading through its softness, cradling the back of her head.

Beneath the thin gown her body clamored for his touch; her breasts swelled with longing, and her body arched toward his. It was the most exquisite torture, Leslie thought in a daze, to be so close to him, to long for caresses that he did not give. A little moan rose to her throat, and her lips sought his again, her body pressing close to him.

This time his kiss was more urgent, and as his mouth devoured hers, one of his hands trailed down her throat and across her bare shoulder to hover over the breast, which by now had almost completely escaped the gown. As his fingers closed around her yielding flesh, Leslie shivered in anticipation. Her hand moved on his chest, down the dark line of hair until it was stopped by his belt buckle.

His kiss grew more intense, his lips hard against her own, and the hands that caressed her grew more urgent. Then suddenly he pulled her to her feet. Weakly she leaned against him as his hands sought the zipper on her dress and it fell in a soft swish to her feet. His lips moved in a burning line down her throat to the erect nipples, rosy in the firelight. Leslie supported herself with trembling hands on his shoulders as he sank to his knees, his hands sure and steady as the lacy panties joined the gown on the floor.

Then he was on his feet again, his arms holding her close, and his belt buckle bit into her tender flesh. Almost to her own surprise, she reached to unbuckle it. Her fingers were unsteady, but they accomplished their task, and his slacks hit the floor with a thud to reveal that under them he wore absolutely nothing. For one long moment Leslie stood staring at him—all male there in the firelight.

Suddenly he swung her up in his arms and carried her toward the great bed in the corner, where he threw himself down beside her, his hands and his mouth raising her to new heights of excitement. Expertly he caressed the pliant body that moved so ardently under his hand. Blindly, without thought, Leslie let herself be swept away, let herself be lost in this vortex of emotion.

Finally, through her waves of longing, she felt him seeking entry, and she steeled herself for the inevitable pain. Even so she could not help crying out as he broke through, and she felt his momentary hesitation. But she clutched at his shoulders, her body moving beneath his, until she felt his renewed ardor. She heard his labored breathing in her ear. Her fingers moved spasmodically on his bare back as her body yearned against him. And then came the intrusion of an alien sound, the creak of an opening door. His body froze against hers.

"Ricky, baby." A throaty voice came through the darkness. "What'cha doing up here all by your lonesome? Little Estelle come to keep you com– comp'ny."

Leslie, looking up at the dark face above her, heard the barely audible curse. Then his eyes warned her to silence. The fire had died down, and the big bed lay deep in shadow as Rick climbed out of it. She shivered once, convulsively, as he drew away from her, and then she lay still, her body aching from loss of contact.

"What are you doing here, Estelle?" he asked as he moved out into the room.

"Come keep comp'ny," Estelle repeated.

From the dark corner where she lay Leslie could see Rick silhouetted against the firelight. And then a female figure approached him. There was the rustle of silk as something slipped to the floor.

"Cut it out, Estelle. I told you never to come here like this. This is *my* place, and I want to be alone. Understand?"

"Sure, baby. Estelle understands. Wanna play."

The slurred voice plainly revealed the woman's drunkenness—and yearning. Leslie swallowed suddenly. How

106

horrible to have to beg like that. To debase herself before the man.

The fire blazed up at that moment, and Leslie bit back an exclamation. Estelle Lamprey was stark naked. She swayed toward Rick, and instinctively he reached out to catch her. Leslie, wide-eyed in the bed, watched the blending of the two bodies in an embrace, stared in appalled silence as two arms hooked themselves around Rick Donovan's neck and pulled his head down. There was something utterly obscene about it, the blending of the body that had just left hers with that of the drunken naked girl. Leslie tasted bile, and without thinking she leaped from the bed and made blindly for the door.

She heard his exasperated "Leslie, wait!" but she knew she was going to be dreadfully sick, and she ran toward the bushes, where moments later her stomach gave up its contents.

The lapping of the water against the shore came with a soothing sound to her distraught senses. That was it. The water. The water would wash away this terrible feeling of distress. It would ease the heat of her body. Blindly she stumbled toward it and threw herself into its welcome coolness. Without thought, she struck out toward the center of the lake, her arms pulling her automatically through the water. She passed the wooden raft, a white blob in the moonlight, but it meant nothing to her. Her only thought was to put as much space as possible between herself and Rick Donovan.

Finally her arms gave out, and she rolled over to float on her back. She was being childish about the whole thing; she saw that clearly. It was certainly no news to her that Rick had had many women, Estelle among them. But to see them like that, their naked bodies blending into each other, when her own body still bore the imprint of his embrace—that had been too much for her.

She had made a mistake, Leslie admitted to herself there

in the darkness. This weekend had proved to be far more than she had bargained for. Her first impulse was to make her way to shore, find a phone, and call Paul. But she could not go running around the countryside stark naked. Nor could she just disappear, leaving Rick to wonder if she were dead or alive. She would have to return to the cabin. She would face him calmly, she told herself, and tell him that the weekend was over, that she wanted to return to Helena right away. He would probably be angry; she realized that. But there seemed no other way out. She could not return to his embrace. The thought filled her with revulsion.

A cool breeze hit the exposed areas of Leslie's body, and she shivered. The water was getting colder, and the shore was some distance away. Fortunately the moonlight was bright enough so that she could make out the landmarks. Rolling over, she struck out toward them. But the water had been colder than she realized, and her right leg cramped. Leslie put down her first panic. A cramp was simple to deal with. That she was naked in the dark in the middle of a strange lake did not alter that fact one bit. She let her face fall into the water, hanging loose in a dead man's float, while she massaged the offending leg.

She thought she had fixed it, but when she struck out again, it returned worse than ever. Leslie slid into the dead man's position again, lifting her head periodically to breathe. It was a nuisance, she told herself, but nothing to panic about. The cramp would leave eventually, and when it did she would swim ashore. A person could stay afloat indefinitely using the dead man. It was all a question of not panicking.

Several minutes later she was considering turning over and trying a backstroke, when something tangled in her hair. The unexpectedness of it made her open her mouth, and of course, she went under, swallowing a lot of water. But the thing in her hair dragged her cruelly to the surface, and she opened her eyes to see Rick Donovan's angry features peering at her from a rubber raft. His face did what the cramp had not been able to do, and she struck out at him in blind panic. "Let me go!"

A smart clip along the jaw knocked her momentarily senseless, and when she came to she was lying across the raft, her flesh quivering with cold.

"What a stupid thing to do," he said harshly. He lay beside her on the narrow raft, his face even with hers. "You might have drowned out here."

She crossed her arms over bare breasts in an effort to stop shaking. "I was perfectly all right. I was going to swim back in a few minutes."

"Sure. That's why you've been in the same place for the last ten minutes, your hair floating out like spilled sunshine on the water."

She was too distraught to hear the anxiety in his voice. "I'm perfectly able to take care of myself," she insisted. "I was coming back."

"You should never have left in the first place. There was no reason."

"No reason!" Leslie's indignation made her voice sharp, but the chattering of her teeth could be heard in the still night air.

"We'll discuss all that later," he said. "After we get back to the fire. Now lie still. If you spill us into the water again, I've a mind to leave you there."

"What—what are you going to do?" she stammered.

"I'm going to lie on top of you," he said calmly, "and paddle this raft back to shore. That's why I brought it. It's much easier than dragging you through the water. Besides, I didn't know what shape you'd be in when I found you."

His features were implacable, and Leslie did not protest as he shifted his weight to cover hers. She had a moment's terror as she realized that he was as naked as she. He had evidently rushed out to find her without pausing for his trunks. His body was wet against hers, but it was wonderfully warm.

"Keep your head still," he ordered. "I'll rest my chin on this side so I can see."

"All right." She murmured the words, her eyes settling on the strong hollow of his throat. He had come after her; even though he knew she could swim like a fish, he had come after her.

Gradually her body lost some of its chill and then, to her chagrin, it welcomed the feel of his for another reason. Lying rigid there as he paddled the raft toward shore, she examined her feelings. It had been brought home to her in the most striking way what kind of man this was. Wouldn't it be far better to break it off now? Another wave of chills swept over her, and she bit her bottom lip to keep her teeth from chattering.

"Easy, Leslie. We're almost there now."

And moments later, true to his words, she felt the raft hit the sand. Her teeth began to chatter uncontrollably as he lifted his body from hers. She tried to rise to one knee, but her leg refused to cooperate and before she could try again, his arm slid under her, and he got to his feet. She put her arms around his neck and buried her head in his shoulder as he carried her up the beach to the cabin.

There was no one else in sight as he put her on the rug and built the fire to a roaring blaze. Then he toweled her briskly and wrapped her in the fur throw, his hands moving expertly to massage the cramp away. Leslie lay there in silence until he had finished.

Then he opened one side of the throw and lay down beside her. She tried to pull away, but he did not allow it, rolling over to throw one arm across her breasts. "Better now?" he said, his lips against her ear.

"Warmer." She was acutely conscious of the male body

so close to her own, but she could not banish the picture of Estelle Lamprey in the arms that now held her.

His lips moved down her throat and then up across her cheek to her mouth. "I want to go back to Helena," she said. The words seemed overloud in the silent room.

He nibbled at the corner of her mouth. "Sure, babe. Tomorrow."

"No. Tonight." With supreme effort she kept her body from melting toward his.

"Be reasonable, Leslie." His voice was still soft and low, in itself a caress. "You'll spoil our weekend."

"It isn't ours!" The words burst from her and she threw his arm aside and leaped to her feet. "I've changed my mind," she cried. "I want to go back. Now!"

He got to his feet and stood facing her. "Leslie, simmer down. So you're upset about Estelle. She knows better than to pull a stupid stunt like that." His features grew harsh. "She knew damn well I had someone else here. She wanted to break it up."

"Well, she certainly succeeded. Don't!" she cried as he took a step toward her. "Don't you touch me!"

"Les–lie." He was clearly trying to be patient. "This is ridiculous. Come on, now." He reached out a hand. "Let's sit down and talk."

"No! I want to leave now." She turned to retrieve her dress, lying across a chair. "I'll get my things."

That was her mistake. In three strides he crossed the distance between them and grabbed her by the shoulders. "You're not going anywhere, Leslie. Not half-hysterical like this."

"Let me go!" She struck out at him blindly, but he jerked her arms behind her and kept them there with one big hand around her wrists.

"You've just got a case of virginal nerves. You'll get over them."

She tried to kick him then. "You needn't make it sound like an accusation."

He did not answer her, his features contracting grimly, as he bent her body toward him. At that moment she felt nothing for him but rage. She tried to twist away from him, but his hands were strong, and he molded her slenderness against his hardness, his lips seeking hers. She turned her head to avoid him, but he buried one hand in her hair and forced her face toward him. "Don't fight me so, baby. We'll fix it. You'll see."

Then his lips met hers. She fought him; with all the strength of anger and outrage, she fought him. But if anything, her resistance seemed to urge him on, and when he swung her up in his arms, kicking and screaming, he simply ignored the blows she rained on him until he reached the great bed.

Rather than release her he threw himself down with her under him and there, while she wept and raged and pleaded, he methodically finished what he had begun. Leslie, tears streaming down her cheeks, dug her nails into his shoulders in a vain effort to stem her own response. But the convulsive shudder that enveloped her was evidence enough for him, and soon she felt his own shudder of consummation.

To her surprise he did not immediately move, but kept his weight on her, gently kissing her salty eyelids and cheeks. "I'm sorry about this, babe. But it's like falling off the proverbial horse. I couldn't let you run off like that."

"There were other ways to stop me," she managed. "You didn't have to—"

"Didn't I?" The moonlight had moved, and now it lay across his face. "If I'd let you go tonight, you'd have never let me near you again. Nor any other man probably."

Silently she admitted the truth of this. "It was unfair of you."

He shrugged. "Sorry about that." He pushed a lock of

112

hair out of her eyes. "You'll find that there's a lot of unfairness in this old world."

He smiled. "Now, if I move will you promise to stay put? I've got you all nicely warmed, and I want you to stay that way. There's always the possibility of a chill after exposure like that."

Leslie nodded. "I won't run off."

"Good." He rolled over, pulling her close against his side. She fought the response in her body and lay quiescent against him. They were silent for some time, and she had almost dozed off, when he spoke, "You know, Leslie, you rather surprise me."

"It wasn't that I didn't have any chances," she said sleepily, her mouth against the hollow of his throat. "It's just—I didn't have much time for men."

"I'm flattered," he said. "I thought there were no more virgins left in the world." His voice carried amusement. "But that wasn't what I was talking about."

"Oh? Then what surprises you about me?" She was wide awake now.

"Well, here you are, the perfect opportunity for a little pillow talk—your chance to save the Golden Star—and you don't even mention the subject." He chuckled dryly. "Don't you know that the best time to hit a man up for something is right after he's been satisfied?"

Leslie grimaced. "I think that's disgusting." She giggled suddenly. "Anyhow, wouldn't it be more sensible to do it *before* he gets what he wants?"

Rick laughed, genuine amusement in his words. "For a cold fish, baby. But for you? Uh-uh." His fingers stole up her side and moved softly over her breast. "All he'd have to do would be to get close enough, and you'd forget the bargain. He'd have what he wanted. Better to hit him up afterward, when his defenses are down."

"Thank you for the advice." Leslie muffled a little moan as his searching fingers found her nipple. "But I don't

113

think I'll bother with it. I'm perfectly capable of taking care of myself. So I won't have to ask a man for anything."

"Not even this?" he asked, covering her mouth again, his body heavy on hers. And she was helpless to control the longing that welled up in her, longing so strong that her body seemed actively to be seeking his caresses, as her mouth lifted of its own accord for his kisses.

CHAPTER 7

The wild caroling of birds woke Leslie early the next morning. Through the large glass windows that fronted the lake, she saw the sparkle of the rising sun on the water. The air was still chilly, and she welcomed the warmth of the man as he lay beside her, his arm thrown over her body, his cheek pillowed against her breast.

She could see only the top of his head, the dark unruly hair rumpled there. And beneath the light blanket that covered them she felt the warmth of his hand as it lay against her side. What would it be like to wake this way *every* morning? Warm in the embrace of the man she loved? Scalding tears welled up in her eyes at the thought. She was being ridiculous. She did not love Rick Donovan. And even if she did, marriage was not part of his life plan. Not now, at least, and never to a nobody like Leslie Jordan.

She blinked rapidly, but several tears could not be contained and slipped down her cheeks to add their saltiness to that of the night before. She struggled to hold back a sob. She was forgetting all her good resolutions. It was Maggie who had loved a man she couldn't have. Leslie Jordan was smarter than that—much smarter.

The hand that lay against her began to move, making long trails up and down her side. "Good morning," he said, his mouth against her breast.

"Good morning." She tried to keep her words even, not to reveal to him what that hand was doing to her.

"What'll it be for breakfast?" he asked, raising his head so quickly that she was unable to mask her disappointment at the thought of leaving his side. He laughed and shook his head. "Eating comes later, Leslie, much later. We have other things to do first."

"I didn't mean—" she faltered, knowing full well that she had.

"Don't be ashamed, Leslie." The blue eyes were serious now. "You've got a great body. It'll serve you well. And now that you recognize its potential you won't have to starve it."

She did not tell him that this experience was going to be her last for a long time, that the thought of another man's hands on her made her stomach surge in revulsion. He would not understand that.

Some demon in her made her say instead, "Paul will appreciate that." She was so shocked at having made such a statement, knowing as she did that she would not do any such thing with Paul, that for a moment she did not realize that a strange look had crossed his face.

When he spoke, his voice was strained. "I'd forget about him."

"But why?" She didn't know what made her go on. "Didn't you just tell me not to starve myself? And he's right there. So convenient."

The hands that spanned her waist tightened cruelly. "I don't like him," Rick said.

Leslie laughed, a brittle sound. "So what? I can't say that I like your Miss Lamprey either. But that doesn't mean anything."

"Now you're being stupid. Estelle is a friend." His hands still gripped her waist.

"So is Paul. And a much nicer person from what I can see."

"Nicer?" He raised himself on one elbow, his eyes scanning her face cruelly. "Nicer, is it? You little idiot. That's precisely why you had to wait so long. He's too damned nice."

Leslie shook her head. "That's not true."

"No?" He pulled himself up to face her, his naked body sliding along her flesh in a way that sent it quivering. "Nice isn't what you want, Leslie. You want a man. A real man."

"Like you, I suppose." She glared into the smoldering blue eyes. "A man who takes a woman against her will."

His jaw hardened. "I never did that in my life," he replied, "And you know it."

"And last night?" The weight of his naked body against her was arousing her.

"Last night you were willing." He grinned sardonically. "At least, you were willing when I did the deed."

Stubbornly she mustered all her defenses. "Well, I'm not willing now." She could not know that her blue-green eyes lay open to him, that desire glittered in their depths. "So if you'll just move, I'll get up and wash."

He was silent for so long that she thought he meant to do as she had asked and disappointment began to creep over her. Then he shook his head. "No dice, Leslie. This is my game. We play by my rules."

She tried to twist out from under him then, knowing that she did not want to succeed, knowing excitement from the feel of his body, warm and vibrant against hers.

"No, Leslie, I always have sex before breakfast." He grinned at her again. "You wouldn't want me to break the habit of a lifetime."

She turned her head sideways to avoid his kisses, but his lips on her throat and cheek were tantalizing. He nibbled at her ear, and when she twisted her head to escape him, he captured her lips. His mouth was hard, demanding, forcing hers open and insisting on compliance from her.

117

Part of her mind rejected this caveman approach, but her body responded to it eagerly, and another part of her mind agreed that he was right. Paul could never raise this kind of animal passion in her, this urgent desire for the feel of his flesh.

Rick kissed her until she panted for breath, his body hard against hers. And when she lay pliant beneath him, he raised his head. "Do you want me to get up now, Leslie?" he asked hoarsely.

"No, no." She hardly recognized her own voice as she pulled his face down to hers.

The sun was fairly high in the sky before Rick left the bed to prepare breakfast. Leslie lay there for some moments longer, her body wonderfully content, drowsily trying to summon the will to get up.

The next thing she knew Rick was kissing her gently. "Breakfast, sleepyhead. Got to refuel the old machine. Especially when you give it so much exercise."

Smiling, she pulled herself up against the headboard and prepared to eat.

"Scrambled eggs," Rick said, putting a plate on the bed table that had suddenly appeared out of nowhere. "Bacon, toast, strawberry jam. Tea and coffee."

"A feast." Leslie smiled at him. How charming he could be, she thought. And how ruthlessly demanding.

"One of my diverse talents," he said, preening himself.

Leslie looked at his naked body, bronzed brown except for the somewhat paler part that marked where his trunks went. "Don't you wear clothes out here?"

He grinned. "Not when I don't have to. The beach is private. That's why the sections of brush run down almost to the water as they do. The sand I had trucked in. These beaches are really stony. Sometimes I skinny-dip, and I often lie naked in the sun. And inside I hardly ever wear clothes. Unless I get cold."

"Don't you get—" Leslie hesitated, embarrassed by the

question, yet wanting to ask it. "Doesn't being without your clothes make you—think about sex?"

He laughed and pressed a kiss into her palm. "Doll baby, everything makes me think about sex!"

She laughed along with him, but there was a curious little pain in her heart. This experience that had been such a wonder for her, was for him just another fun weekend. In six months he would not even remember her name. By that time there would have been a long line of successors moving through this cabin and his life. But for her, she knew, it would be different. There would be no forgetting for her. If only Maggie had left more of the diary, some indication of how to go on when you were forced to leave behind the man you wanted to spend your life with.

"Penny," Rick said.

She flushed slightly. "Oh, nothing. I'll have tea, please, with cream." She turned her attention to the eggs and bacon.

"Where do you go from here?" he asked, as they finished up the crumbs.

Leslie was startled. "What do you mean?"

"Obviously you aren't going to make your life's work writing about Helena."

"No, of course not. We've got a day or two to wind it up, then it's back to Cleveland."

"No more Montana sun," he teased.

Leslie shrugged. "One has to eat. And I like my work."

"Do you make trips like this often?"

She nodded. "Pretty often. Though usually they're closer to Cleveland."

He put the bed table on the floor and joined her on the bed, his bronzed body making a striking contrast against the white sheets. Automatically Leslie's hand reached out to play with the crisply curling hair on his chest, and he turned toward her, pulling her into the circle of his arm. His chin rested on the top of her head, and one hand moved lazily up and down her body in absentminded caresses as he asked, "How about a couple hours of sailing before we start back?"

"Sure." The one word was all that Leslie could manage. She had been trying to forget that soon their time together would be finished, that he would walk out of her life just as easily as he had walked into it.

"Or maybe you'd rather lie in the sun," he continued. "A hardworking girl like you doesn't get much chance to develop a tan."

Leslie swallowed hard. She did not want to sail; she did not want to lie in the sun. She wanted to spend the few precious hours she had left close against the body that had become so familiar to her. But she did not say so. To speak so openly of her desire was beyond her capacity.

He kissed the top of her head. "Which'll it be?"

"The beach, I think." She met his eyes squarely. "I feel like a lazy day."

Rick grinned. "Not too lazy, I hope." Then with a quick grin he got to his feet. "Let's go for a swim."

"As soon as I get my suit."

He shook his head. "Come on, live a little. No suits."

"But, Rick!"

"This is a private beach," he said, a devilish merriment in his eyes. "We won't go out far. After all, you've already done it. Then we'll come up and lie in the sun, and I'll rub you all over with oil. So that white skin won't burn."

The words were inviting, his look even more so, but still Leslie hesitated. He grabbed her hand and pulled her into his arms. "Rick, put me down. Please!"

"Nope. And don't yell too loud, or you'll have an audience out there. The cabin muffles sound, but the water makes it carry."

Knowing that she was unable to convince him, she hooked her arms around his neck and hung on. She would experience whatever this weekend held for her. Forgetting could not be made harder by today. She already knew the feel of his body against hers, the kisses and caresses that made her body so vibrantly alive.

He carried her down the little beach and straight out into the water. She felt the heat of the sun on her bare body, and then he was standing thigh deep in the water, a diabolic grin on his face. "I can't decide whether to lower you gradually or just drop you."

Leslie shivered automatically, recalling how icy the water had seemed the night before. "I—" she began, but at that precise moment he plunged into the water, lowering both of them to their necks. Leslie squealed as the cold water hit her skin, and her arms fell away from his neck. But his hands did not release her, and when her feet found the bottom and she could stand, his hands were still warm on her waist.

"Let's walk out a little," he said, pulling her near, and arms around each other, they walked out until the water reached Leslie's breasts. It was a strange sensation, feeling the water against skin that had always been covered before. Of course, she had been naked in the lake the night before. But then her mind had been a whirl of confused emotion; there had been no room in it for sensuous impressions. Now, as Rick stopped and turned to face her, she felt the water lapping gently against her skin.

"See now," he said, smiling. "Isn't this great?"

Leslie nodded. "The water feels good. And the sun." She tilted her head back to look up at the brilliant blue sky. "I just can't get over how bright and blue it is. Cleveland's sky is gray so much of the time."

She brought her eyes back to his face and was surprised to find there a look of admiration that made her flush. "You're a beautiful woman, Leslie," he said, his eyes moving over her face and breasts. "With your hair all tangled and fallen like that you look like some Aphrodite newly risen from the sea."

"Isn't she supposed to be on a seashell and covering herself in a maidenly fashion with her hands?" Leslie tried for a light tone; the air between them was heavy with sexual electricity.

He smiled, but his eyes remained serious. "I suppose you're thinking of Botticelli's Venus. I've always thought her a rather insipid little thing. No, I was thinking of a Venus with hair like tangled seaweed and pink-nippled breasts just tantalizingly evident above the sea's foam."

Leslie lowered her eyes, feeling the tears coming, hot and scalding. No one had ever paid her such a lovely compliment before, no man had ever made her feel so alive, so vibrantly aware of herself as a woman.

She swallowed hastily. "Thank you, sir. And which god are you?" she asked brightly, trying not to show how deeply his words had affected her.

One hand reached up to curl a wet strand of her hair around his finger while with the other he drew her closer. There were only inches between their naked bodies, and even through the water she felt the heat of him.

"You tell me," he said.

She managed a little laugh. "Zeus?"

He shook his head. "No, I'm fickle and I like power, but I don't want a wife, especially one like Hera who couldn't leave anything male alone."

Leslie, her hands on his bare shoulders, looked up into the darkly handsome face. "Apollo?"

This time Rick smiled. "Thank you for the compliment. Apollo was known for his good looks. Though I always think of the classical Greeks as fair-haired. Perhaps it's because of the marble statues. They give an effect of lightness. But what do you know about Apollo?"

"He was very handsome," Leslie replied. "And wasn't he the god of the sun?" She ran a finger across his bare bronzed shoulder. "That certainly fits."

Rick's eyes were merry. "And what about his other

122

accomplishments—poetry, prophecy, healing, music, and wisdom. What about them?"

Leslie shook her head. "That's a large order. Looks like Apollo was a god of many parts."

This elicited the chuckle she had hoped for. "Well," she continued, "I've never heard you sing, but I imagine you have a good voice. That should take care of music. As for poetry, though I can't imagine you writing sad sonnets, the compliment you paid me was very poetic." She paused.

"Medicine," he prompted.

Some demon inside her caused her to say, "You're very good with female hysteria." She was somewhat shocked at her own words, but he laughed appreciatively.

"And prophecy and wisdom?"

Leslie frowned. "I'm afraid that there you don't fit the bill."

"I foretold a great weekend, didn't I?"

She smiled. "Yes, I'll have to grant you that."

"And I'm wise in the ways of the world."

Too wise, Leslie longed to say, but instead she replied, "I don't think that's the kind of wisdom we're talking about. For instance, you're not at all wise about the preservation of this state's heritage."

His grin didn't falter. "That's a matter of opinion, my dear." He dropped a kiss on the tip of her nose. "At any rate I came off better in this god business than I had expected."

"How?" she asked curiously.

"I thought you might see me as Hades. You know, the one the Romans called Pluto, god of the underworld and night. Because of my darkness and because—" His eyes began to smolder. "Certain other things—"

Leslie, her eyes locked with his, spoke softly. "Hades. Pluto. He stole Persephone from her mother, Ceres, didn't he?"

Rick nodded. "Ceres was her Roman name. The Greeks called her Demeter." His eyes caressed her. "Persephone was a virgin. And Hades kept her for four months underground with him, letting her return to her mother for the other eight. While she was gone Demeter mourned, causing winter, but when the girl returned Demeter's happiness erupted into spring."

Leslie, with new knowledge of her sexuality, wondered that springtime should return to the world when it did. If the story had been written by a woman in love, she told herself silently, spring would have come instead with her return to the arms of the man who loved her.

For a long moment there was silence between them, and then suddenly he crushed her against him. She gasped at the contact of their bodies, the feel of her naked breasts against his chest. But there was little time to consider the difference in her sensual reactions, for he had tilted back her head and was taking her lips. Her body molded itself willingly to his. When his mouth left hers, it traveled along her cheek to her ear. "Let's do it out here," he whispered.

"Rick!" Leslie had known that such things occurred, but she had certainly never thought *she* would be doing them. "We can't! Not out here! Not in broad daylight!"

His grin was devilish. "Can't we? Let's see." His arms clasped her tightly as he walked off into deeper water. She could not escape his grasp, and soon the ground fell away from her feet.

"Rick, you're crazy." She realized that in spite of her protests the idea was exciting, but she could not tell him that.

He smiled. "Not crazy, just a little different, babe. Hang on now." And covering her lips with his, he pulled her under the water.

It was a whole new experience, being kissed so, and when they surfaced Leslie forgot to protest anymore. They were, after all, in water up to their necks. No one could really see what they were doing.

"Now," he said, his hands spanning her waist, "just follow my directions. You're in for a new experience."

He paused, startled by the look on her face. For his words had come so naturally, so freely, that until the last sentence she had not been thinking of the many other women who had been at his cabin, who had obviously done this same thing with him. Without thinking, she tried to disentangle herself from his arms.

But he would not release her. "Come on, Leslie." His lips caressed her face. "You're a big girl now. You knew about my life-style before you agreed to come."

He was right, of course, but how could she have known about this sickening feeling in the pit of her stomach at the thought of his being with another woman? She had had no experience to build on, no way to know that though she didn't love him, though she had come merely to have fun, she would feel this sense of loss at the thought of him being with someone else.

Obviously her face was revealing her feelings, for he tangled his hand in her wet hair, holding her head steady, and kissed her thoroughly. Though she considered trying to resist him, Leslie soon surrendered. Her body was quick now to react to his caresses, and as he seemed to remember exactly what affected her most, it wasn't long before she was clinging to him weakly and obeying his whispered orders.

With her legs wrapped around his waist and her arms hooked about his neck, she surrendered to the feelings he aroused in her, wondering only idly what would happen if she forgot and let go of him. And then the wonder came crashing in upon her, and all she could do was bury her head in his shoulder and lose herself in it.

When she became aware of her surroundings again, she saw with surprise that he was standing only waist-deep in the water. "It's easier when there's less water pressure," he explained, noting her expression. He grinned. "I learned the hard way not to get too far out. It's sort of a shock to a woman to go under at a time like that."

Leslie nodded, feeling some embarrassment as she unwrapped her legs and felt the sand once more beneath her feet. She was getting her breath back and with it came curiosity. "I don't see how you can—" She stopped. "I mean, I get so carried away."

"I get the question, Leslie." He took her hand and began to walk toward the beach. "I don't."

"But—"

He smiled. "Surely you know how great a woman's capacity is."

She nodded.

"Well, most women really enjoy that experience. And I enjoy their enjoyment." He laughed. "If I let go of myself out there, we'd both come up sputtering. And that's not very romantic, now is it?"

Leslie had to smile at the picture he made. "No, I guess not."

"Don't worry about me. We'll do it again. Later, on the beach."

"On the beach?" Surprise made her voice uneven.

"Sure. It's my beach. And it's private."

"But . . . people on the lake? Airplanes?"

"Leslie." His grin was understanding. "People on the lake aren't going to sail that close to shore. And airplanes. How much can you see from an airplane?"

"I–I don't know." He would have answers for all her arguments, she knew that. And she had to admit that her body was already responding to the idea.

"You'll see. I'll spread the blanket and cover you all over with oil." His hand slipped down from her waist to pat her bottom. "What a pleasure that will be. And then, when you're all nicely oiled and warmed by the sun—" He grinned brashly. "You can oil me."

Leslie, her knees trembling, found she could not answer him. The sand was warm against her toes, and she tried to concentrate on that rather than think about her nakedness. Still, she was glad to lie down when Rick spread out the blanket. At least when she was prone, she felt less visible to those on the lake.

"Back or front first?" asked Rick.

Leslie lay on her stomach. "Back," she mumbled, unable to face him.

Pushing her hair out of the way, he began with her shoulders, pouring the oil in his palm and then smoothing it over her skin in long, practiced strokes. The feel of it was incredibly sensuous, and Leslie lay quite still, all her feelings centered on the sensitive skin beneath his fingers. She felt curiously relaxed and yet paradoxically more alive than ever before.

As his fingers moved lower and lower she found it more and more difficult to control her response to him. And when finally he told her to roll over, her hesitation was too pronounced not to be noted. "Time to roll over," he said again, his voice lightly teasing.

And Leslie rolled. A quiver went over her as he brushed away some grains of sand that clung to her perspiring flesh. "Now, the front," he said.

She closed her eyes, but not before she saw the mischief in his face that told her he knew her embarrassment and was amused by it. The sun beat down on her naked body. She could tell from the sudden coolness where his shadow fell upon her. His hands moved smoothly, gently, tenderly, and every stroke, though it distributed the oil over her heated body, was also a persuasive caress, raising in her a prolonged yearning. By the time he had finished, she was coated with oil, her body silky and sensuous.

He bent over and kissed her lightly. "Now it's your

turn." Her eyes flew open at the touch of his lips and encountered his eyes only inches away. Strange fires seemed to burn deep in their vivid blue depths, fires that set her own blood aflame. She closed her eyes again, but he did not let her rest. "Come on, none of that."

Obediently she opened her eyes and discovered that he was sitting back on his heels. Of its own accord her gaze went to his manhood. Catching the look, he laughed. Then, pressing the bottle of oil into her hands, he flopped over onto his stomach. "Every inch," he ordered. "I want to be as slippery as a greased pig."

Leslie giggled at the image, some of her nervousness vanishing. "Yes, sir." She poured oil in a long trail down his bare back, where it gleamed against the bronzed skin. On her knees she massaged the oil into him, watching the play of muscles under her fingers, marveling at the sheer beauty of his body, the broad sinews of his shoulders, the long rippling muscles that traversed his back. When she approached the band of slightly lighter skin that was ordinarily hidden under his trunks, her hand shook only slightly.

"Ahhhhhh." A muffled sound of appreciation came from the vicinity of his head. "You have wonderful hands, Aphrodite," he murmured.

Leslie's hands moved down his legs. Her palms sensitive to the crisp hair, she rubbed the oil into his legs, admiring as she did so their tempered musculature. There was no denying it. Rick Donovan's body was practically perfect. For a moment she felt a fierce longing to throw herself down on that beautiful body, to feel it against hers. Then her hands resumed their task.

If only his character were better. . . . She stopped such thinking immediately. After today, his character was not going to be of any concern to her.

He was fun to be with, and he knew how to treat a woman. As for the rest of it—his refusal to face love and commitment, and the vulnerability they implied—she really could not blame him. Wasn't she doing the same thing?

He rolled over then, without waiting for her to tell him to, and lay looking up at her. The expression on his face was one of desire, and her hands trembled as she clasped the oil and moved up beside him. The air between them was electric. Rick reached out to stroke her arm. "Isn't this fun?" he asked softly.

Leslie nodded. Fun was not the word she would have used, but she was busy soaking up all the sensations of her body, every nerve of which seemed to be pulsing with a life of its own. For a moment, looking down into his eyes, she felt a magnetic pull, but she was still too unsure of herself to initiate a kiss. And so she poured oil onto his bronzed chest, watching it puddle in little pools around the crinkly curly chest hair. Then, fingers fluttering, she stroked it in.

"Are you sure you've never been a masseuse?" Rick asked without opening his eyes.

"I'm sure," Leslie replied. "All this is quite new to me." She poured oil over the lean, taut stomach, moving slightly so that her back was toward him as she massaged the oil into the paler skin. She knew the flush on her face was not caused by the sun. But how was she to react when faced with this hard proof of his maleness?

Then she was moving rapidly on down his body, relishing the feel of his hard-muscled legs. She took a long time with them, then finally put the cap on the oil. "All done," she announced.

He opened one eye. "Good. Now lie down and get some sun. You'll be even more beautiful with an allover tan." He winked at her. "It really turns a man on to see that kind of tan and picture a woman naked on the beach. A woman like that can have any man she wants."

Obediently Leslie lay down beside him. She felt the grains of sand that had fallen on the blanket, gritty beneath her. The sun beat down relentlessly, and she shaded her eyes with one upraised arm, aware as she did so that this made her breast even more prominent. Beads of perspiration stood out on her upper lip, and she swallowed nervously. It was impossible to relax with him lying there so close beside her, so completely and blatantly male. She forced herself to breath deeply, to concentrate on her physical reactions to the sun and the sand. She would forget Rick entirely and lose herself in her sensations.

She began to make an inventory of her body. The oil was warm and slippery between her toes and fingers, giving a curious sensation whenever she moved them against each other. Under her right shoulder was a bump, something in the sand under the blanket. She shifted slightly to accommodate herself to it and felt the grating of several grains of sand under her left hip. Her arms and legs, already glowing from yesterday's exposure, were warmed by the sun. But her exposed breasts and the narrow strip of flesh that her bikini had covered yesterday seemed far warmer. She grew hotter and hotter, her body throbbing in places where the sun's rays would never reach.

She took down the arm that covered her face and stretched them both out at her sides. Supine, she lay there, offering her body to the sun. Floating in a haze of sensation, Leslie's mind came to rest on their earlier talk of gods and goddesses. If he was Apollo, god of the sun, she was most surely an offering to him, lying there immobile until the god took his will of her. The image fascinated her. How strange that there were no pagan rites in which women offered themselves naked to the all-powerful sun. There was certainly an erotic element to the idea. Her body, already aroused, tingled at the thought. She searched her mind for fragments of information. Some Indian tribe, was it the Aztecs or the Incas?, worshiped the sun and practiced human sacrifice. Did they burn their victims? She could not remember.

Her imaginings were leading her in rather gory directions, she thought, becoming again aware of the heat of the sun on her body. A cool breeze from the lake moved suddenly over her, and Leslie sighed deeply. It was like the caress of a lover's hand, that little breeze. How much longer did he expect her to lie there like that, she wondered, her body throbbing as she forced herself to remain still?

After what seemed like an eternity she felt him move on the blanket beside her, but she did not open her eyes. She held her breath, waiting. His touch, when it finally came, was light and fleeting, brushing her quivering flesh first here, then there. "You have sand on you," he said.

Leslie's eyes flew open. His dark face was close to hers and she had a momentary image of the mythical Persephone, an innocent who was helpless in the power of her god-lover. She thought of making some light reply to him, but desire lay so heavy on her that she could not speak.

"You look at me out of those blue-green eyes, Aphrodite, goddess of love." His words were as much a caress as his brief and fleeting kiss, a kiss that he gave without touching her body with his. Leslie licked her lips, tasting salt. She longed to reach up and pull him down on her, but something in his eyes told her that was exactly what he wanted.

"Come, Aphrodite," he coaxed, his face close to hers, "tell me your wishes."

Leslie licked suddenly dry lips. The devil dancing in his eyes told her quite plainly that he knew exactly what he was doing, that this quiet tantalization was just as arousing as any caress, that the very absence of his touch was in itself an exquisite stimulation. "I–I've never been a goddess before," she whispered, her eyes on his.

"It's easy." He reached out to touch her, then withdrew his hand before it got to her. "Goddesses give orders." He smiled. "And their slaves obey."

Leslie shook her head. "I–I don't think I'm a good Aphrodite." Her body was taut with longing, and still she could not reach out to him. "Maybe I make a better Persephone."

He shook his head. "There are two sides to every coin, Leslie. Sometimes a man likes his woman to be aggressive. Tell me what you want."

"I–I can't." She wanted desperately to feel his hard body against her own, but to ask him for that, outright, as Estelle Lamprey had—she simply could not do it.

He frowned in mock severity. "I'm trying to complete your education," he complained. "And you're not cooperating."

She tried to think of some way to explain it to him, but she could not tell him about her feelings. He would not understand them.

He drew back from her. "I'm not going ahead until you tell me what to do. I mean it, Leslie."

She saw that he did, and her body yearned even more for him, but she knew, too, that she could not say so. Not in the blunt way he expected. And then she had an idea. "You said I'm Aphrodite, and I'm to give the orders?"

He nodded. "That's right."

Leslie took a deep breath. "Then these are my orders. You are to think of yourself as Hades, and I am Persephone, newly come to your underworld."

For a moment he looked about to protest, but she repeated firmly. "Those are my orders."

He gazed at her for one long moment while her heart pounded in her throat, and then he smiled. "You are a devious woman, Leslie Jordan. Very devious."

"I am Persephone," she said softly, her eyes pleading with him. "And you–you are my lord."

The words were scarcely out of her mouth before his lips captured hers, and this time he pressed close against her, his body hard on hers. His lips left her mouth and moved to her ear. "You're mine, all mine, little innocent," he whispered. "I'll have the pleasure of your ripe young body. And it will be mine. All mine. Forever."

Leslie, hot tears springing to her eyes, knew the words for part of the game, but was still affected by them. Her body, already aroused, grew hotter still as he kissed and fondled her, whispering little comments in his role of Hades that heightened her already intense feelings.

He took his time, as much time as if she had truly been the complete and unaroused innocent that they pretended her to be. Although she tried to lie passive, playing her part, she could not help the whimpers of passion that came from her lips or the sensuous movement of her body under his skillful hands. And finally when he stretched himself full length upon her, she gasped and clutched convulsively at his shoulders.

"You're mine," he whispered hoarsely against her neck, one hand tangled in her hair. "Admit it. Admit it, Persephone."

Leslie's breath was coming in great gasps. "I–I'm yours," she murmured, knowing the words for the truth.

His lips sought hers, crushing them in his passion. She felt the weight of his body on hers, the wonderful lean hardness of it. But still he did not take her completely. "Surrender to me," he whispered, his breath hot on her throat. "Give me your innocence. Ask me to take it."

And Leslie, lost in their pretense and in the intensity of her feelings, replied, "I'm yours. Oh, please! Take me!"

Then they were one. He took her strongly, almost savagely, yet underlying all was a strange aura of tenderness. Leslie, buffeted by waves of passion even stronger than those of the night before, was only vaguely aware of it, thinking hazily of how well he played the part. Caressing, seducing, persuading, yet all the time confident in his own ability. The culmination came with explosive suddenness, and Leslie, feeling the reaction of his body, knew that he, too, was satisfied.

She lay very still, afraid that any movement would make him move away, reluctant to lose the satisfying feel of his body. He did move finally, rolling over and pulling her close against his side.

"Wow!" He said the word softly, but with great feeling. "Old Hades had a really good thing going there."

"I expect he would have tired of her sooner," Leslie heard herself say, "if they hadn't been separated like that every year."

There was silence for a moment. "Yeah," Rick said, and there was a subtle change in his voice. "A man likes variety."

"Women, too," Leslie replied. She heard herself with some amazement, for she knew quite well that she did not intend to make a habit of this. It would take a very long time before she forgot the feel of Rick Donovan against her. Nor would she be apt to try to erase his memory with the feel of someone else. That would be an exercise in futility.

"You're a quick learner, Leslie." His tone was not an admiring one, and she found herself replying with irritation.

"I had a good teacher. Experienced."

The atmosphere between them was no longer one of relaxation and satisfaction, and Leslie bit her lip to keep back the tears.

Rick glanced up at the sun. "It's getting late. Just time for a quick swim. Then we'll finish up the sandwiches and head back."

Numbly Leslie followed him into the water; all her feelings of contentment had vanished.

CHAPTER 8

When the silver Mercedes drew up before the motel door, Leslie knew this was good-bye. She had for a while nourished the hope that the atmosphere of slightly restrained hostility between them would diminish, but it had not. In fact, it had seemed to increase so, that by the time they reached Helena they were speaking to each other like two strangers. She did not like it, but she did not know what to do about it. And perhaps it was better to part like this. It gave the whole thing a feeling of closure; this was definitely the end.

She turned to him as the car came to a halt. "I want to thank you for the weekend," she said, hating the stiltedness of her voice, but not knowing how to change it. "Your cabin is fabulous, and I had a very good time."

The face he turned to her was not smiling. "You're welcome, I'm sure. I'm always at the service of Aphrodite."

The words were cold, and Leslie could find no reply. She groped for the door handle, but he was out of his seat and around to open her door before she could get out.

He stood there smiling grimly, and she blinked back tears as she climbed out. He reached in for her suitcase and set it on the pavement. There was a moment of strained silence. Leslie, looking down at the pavement, wished only that he would leave while she still had control of herself. Finally she looked up at him, her eyes shining with unshed tears. "I did enjoy myself," she whispered softly. "And I do thank you."

He looked down at her for a long moment, and then, just as she thought he would turn away, he grabbed her roughly by the shoulders, his mouth coming down on hers brutally, demanding her submission, raising again all the feelings she was trying so desperately to lay to rest. Then he held her off again, the blue eyes scornful. "I like you better as Persephone," was his only comment. And then he got back in the car and drove away without another word, without a backward look.

Leslie stood there stunned, her eyes on the retreating Mercedes, until the sound of footsteps on the concrete aroused her. She gathered up her case and made her way numbly to her room. Surely Rick did not end all his weekends like this. There was more to it than studied coldness: she knew that. He was angry, very angry, and she hadn't the slightest idea why.

As she unpacked, her hands moving automatically, she tried to sort it out in her mind. Minute by minute she went over the day. There had been that little irritation early in the morning when she had mentioned Paul. But that had passed quickly. In the water and later on the beach in the sun, there had been tension between them, but it had been purely sexual tension, not like the hostility she had felt later. Her body grew hot as she remembered that scene on the beach. How freely they had entered into the Hades-Persephone fantasy—and how lovely the experience had been. No, it had been something after that that had changed things.

The shrill ring of the phone shattered her concentration, and she turned to it with a frown. "Hello?"

"Leslie! Thank God, you're all right." Paul sounded more than a little upset.

"Of course I'm all right," she replied, rather more sharply than she had intended. "Why shouldn't I be?"

136

"Les–lie." Paul's impatience was evident. "You go off without telling me where. Leaving me nothing but a cryptic note. And I'm not supposed to be upset?"

"Look, Paul, I'm a big girl now. I'm twenty-six years old. I know how to take care of myself."

"Sure." His tone was sarcastic. "You're not fooling me, Les. I know you went off someplace with Donovan. That scum!"

"Mr. Donovan is not scum," Leslie said, thinking how shocked Paul would be if he knew everything that had happened this weekend. "He's a respectable citizen of the community."

"Yeah, sure. So respectable he's had every young woman in Helena."

"Paul, you're exaggerating." She ignored the twinge of pain his words caused. "And, at any rate, Mr. Donovan's life-style is no concern of yours."

"Yours is!" The explosive tone communicated Paul's anger quite effectively.

Leslie felt her patience slipping. "You're wrong, Paul. Our relationship is a professional one. I did think we were friends, but that doesn't give you the right to behave like this. And frankly, I just don't need it."

"Oh, Les. How could you?" The accusation was sharp, and Leslie lost the last shreds of her patience. "That's it, Paul! I've had it! It's my own affair, and I don't intend to discuss it with you anymore. Please understand that. Now, I've had a long and busy weekend. I'm going to have a quiet dinner in my room and then go to bed. I'll meet you for breakfast at eight. Provided you can keep your mind on business. Good night." She returned the phone to the cradle without waiting for his reply.

She waited a moment, then ordered her dinner and turned back to finish her unpacking. The green dress she shoved far back in the closet. She was not sure she would even take it back to Ohio with her. Nor the white bikini.

She considered pitching it into the wastepaper can in the corner. But of course, that wouldn't do any good. She couldn't dispose of her body, and that was where the most memories lay.

She had just finished putting things away when a knock on the door announced the arrival of her dinner. Leslie eyed the food without much appetite, but she forced herself to sit down and eat it. Then with a sigh she put the dirty dishes in the hall outside and closed her door. Through the window she saw the last of the sunlight reflecting off the lake. It was really too early to go to bed, yet she did not want to be with other people. Nor did she want to watch anything on television.

She cast a glance toward the bedside table where Maggie's diary rested in the drawer. Bits and pieces of it were permanently implanted in her memory and other parts she knew exactly where to find, but it had been many years since she'd read the whole thing through. Perhaps that was the thing to do: Take a quick shower and settle down in bed with Maggie's story. It would not make her forget Rick Donovan. But nothing could do that. And she had a terrible need to be close to Maggie again.

She slipped out of her clothes. Yes, that was what she would do. But turning suddenly, she caught sight of her naked body in the mirror and paused. The sun had begun its work, and her skin glowed golden brown; the area that had been covered by her bikini was only a slightly lighter shade. For a long moment Leslie stared at herself. Her body seemed foreign to her, its flat stomach and upturned breasts belonging to someone else. Of course, she had never given her body much attention before. It was there and it functioned—and that was all she cared about. But now it was going to be different: she would have known that even without Maggie's diary. Now she had a body that was awakened, and it would not be easily put to sleep again.

She made her way into the bath and stepped into the shower. Anything and everything reminded her of her time with Rick—the water on her bare skin, the slick feel of the soap like the oil they had used. With a sob she thrust her head under the shower and began to shampoo it fiercely. Though she had washed it just before they had left Whitefish, it seemed to smell of the sun and water, of the pines that grew close to the lake. She toweled it dry as fiercely as she had washed it and began to attack her body in the same manner. But to her horror she discovered that however she touched it she was reminded of Rick Donovan.

Hurrying into the bedroom, she pulled on her nightgown and climbed into the bed. Her hair lay damply against her shoulders, as it had that afternoon by the lake. Leslie pushed it angrily aside as, frowning, she opened the diary. Perhaps by reading Maggie's story through, she could exorcise the image of Rick. She would confront Maggie's words and the image of Mick Donovan, which in her youth she had enshrined in her heart. She would face all that, Leslie told herself sternly. Face it and conquer it.

And so she began. The room around her faded as Maggie's Montana came alive. How excited the poor Irish girl from New York had been to step down from the Wells Fargo stage that day in 1868 and look around at this raw, new country. For Maggie Callahan, city-bred and city-born, Montana was a whole other world. The dirt and rawness were nothing to a girl raised in a tenement. And as the seasons changed, the blue, blue sky, the trees and grass, even the great drifts of white snow, were wonders to her.

The dirty streets of Helena, rutted by the wheels of heavy wagons, teemed with men looking for a new start. Maggie described them all: the burly men and the puny ones, equally intent on wresting wealth from the stubborn earth; the bankers and merchants, the businessmen, who followed to supply the town's needs; the gamblers and cardsharps, saloon owners, waiting to get their share by means fair or foul. Even the obsequious Chinese, washing dirty clothes, working the tailings no one else wanted, were described by Maggie, from their blue-pajama suits to their long queues.

Maggie's pages were alive with little pictures of special men and women; she had a real eye for detail and description. The town, with its stores, false-fronted to distinguish them from quite similar dwellings, came to life for Leslie. She could see the "ladies" from the Castle, taking the air outside that red-brick sporting house at Joliet and State Streets. Young women, as Maggie described them, learning the trade under the tutelage of Chicago Jo, while in other rooms the Duke helped the miners to gamble away their earnings. Maggie's description of the girls—Lilli and Monica and Kim and the rest—was tinged with mixed anger and compassion. She herself, good Catholic that she was, could not condone the selling of a woman's body into sin. Yet she knew firsthand how harsh the world could be to a young woman alone. It was only by the grace of Almighty God and the quick way of learning he had given her that Maggie Callahan herself was not one of those poor creatures. She could dance, Maggie could. And that was her salvation in the rough, tough world.

Leslie read on. The Montana days—vivid blue sky and the everlasting miracle of the sun; Montana nights—the clear sky a blanket of sparkling stars. Maggie's joy in the performances, her awe of the occasional Shakespearean actor and actress, her hearty enjoyment of the comedies.

Here, too, were anecdotes and descriptions of the men who wished to be Maggie Callahan's "fellows." The old dry-goods store owner, the hard bullwhacker, the stolid rancher, the rugged young cowboy. All of them and more had wanted to squire Maggie about, wanted, too, to sample her favors. But Maggie was adamant about that. She was a good Catholic girl, and no matter what other women in the theatre did, she would not give her body so freely. Marriage was what Maggie really wanted. Marriage with a strong, sound man whom she could adore as her darling mother, bless her sainted soul, had adored her father.

And Maggie had a knack. No matter how often she turned them down, those men remained her friends. Yes, life was good for Maggie Callahan. And if she had not yet met her man, well, she was young—she could wait.

And then had come that momentous day when walking out of H. M. Parchen and Company, where she had gone to purchase a new shade for her oil lamp, she had collided with a man. The new shade had gone crashing to the floor, to shatter into many pieces, and Maggie's angry words had stopped in her throat when her eyes met the vivid blue ones of Mick Donovan.

Leslie, recalling that first look that Rick had given her across the theatre, shivered. Just so had his great-grandfather claimed Maggie with a glance. And, thought Leslie with a deep sigh, Maggie had not been naive. For a moment Leslie raised her eyes from the yellowed page. Her heart was already pounding. Was it really wise to stir this all up again?

But she must, she told herself fiercely. It was not Rick who had this hold on her. Rick was not his great-grandfather—and she was not Maggie. She had to read on.

The going was much slower now. Sometimes the tears so filled Leslie's eyes that she couldn't see the faded words and had to pause and use a tissue. Even the descriptions of Maggie's first ecstatic joy were painful to her great-granddaughter. Leslie, reliving her own feelings, was swept by such a wave of longing for Rick that she sobbed aloud. If he had, somehow, walked into the room at that moment, she would have thrown herself so willingly into his arms. But the room remained silent, no welcome knock on the door, nothing but the whisper of turning pages.

Unashamedly, Leslie allowed the tears to fall as Maggie detailed the plans they had made, Mick's lucky strike, and then the weeks of growing suspicion that all was not well, ending with the big Irishman's defection and Maggie's proud withdrawal. Not for Maggie Callahan the secondary position of mistress. Not for her to help a man break his marriage vows. But she knew the limits of her strength, Maggie did, knew that being in the same town with the man she loved could only lead to disaster. And so she left the big land she loved and went back to the gray city.

Leslie closed the book gently. "Oh, Maggie, I've been a fool. I should have learned from your example," she cried. "And I didn't."

For now, with the story of Maggie and Mick so fresh in her mind, she faced a bitter truth. It was not merely physical attraction that pulled her toward Rick Donovan. She wanted the man, that was true, wanted to lie all night in his arms. But as much as she wanted that, she also wanted to spend her life beside him, to erase from those brilliant eyes the hurt she had seen there, to convince him that her love was for the man alone—not his name, not his money. For she did love him. It was an unavoidable fact. It was a fact she did not want to face. But the truth was there, staring at her. If she had not spent the weekend with him, if they hadn't talked—perhaps this would not have happened. One passion-filled night with the Kissing Bandit could have been forgotten—or remembered with pleasure. But she knew too much about Rick now. She had glimpsed the pain behind that hard, polished exterior, and she would not be able to think of him as some conceited rich playboy who deserved his life of emptiness. Her heart

142

ached when she recalled his words of loneliness, words that had awakened painful memories of her own. If only there was some way she could break through that shell and reach the hurting man inside.

Leslie put the diary back in the drawer and turned out the light. The tears welled up in her eyes as she lay there in the darkness. She was not going to be any luckier in love than Maggie had been. And she might as well accept the fact. Even if she had had the courage to pursue Rick, he had made it clear that whatever had been between them was finished—done. And when he was like that, there was no way of reaching him.

She sighed again heavily. There was nothing she could do about Rick, but the Star's fate was not yet sealed. There must be something she could do to help there. It was positively criminal to lose that theatre. If only the people of Helena could see the Star through Maggie's eyes, Leslie thought. To know it as she did. That would make them understand how important it was.

Suddenly Leslie sat bolt upright in the bed. That was it! That was the idea she had been groping for. She turned on the light and reached for the phone book. There it was, Karen Hooper's number.

The phone rang six times, eight times. She was about to hang up when a breathless voice answered. "Hello."

"Karen, this is Leslie. Listen! I just had a great idea about the Star. We can get a lot of public attention for the campaign to save it."

"It must be great, Leslie. You sound really excited."

Something in Karen's tone caused Leslie to hesitate. "Did I interrupt something?" she asked.

Karen's chuckle was warm. "Not exactly, Leslie. Do you happen to have the time?"

Leslie looked at her watch and gasped. "My God, Karen! I'm sorry. It's 1 A.M. I had no idea. I was reading Maggie's diary. Listen, I'll call you back in the morning."

"No, Leslie. Wait." Karen's voice was warm. "I'm awake now. And I won't be able to get back to sleep for wondering about your idea. So tell me."

"I was reading Maggie's diary. And then I thought it was too bad people can't see the Star through Maggie's eyes. And then I had it! They could! I can write a series of articles about the Star, incorporating pieces of Maggie's diary. And each of them can be a push for preservation."

"That's great, Leslie. You might also mention the antique auction on Friday night. I know just the man to call. The owner of one of the city's papers is an old friend and gave the society a good contribution. I'm sure he'll agree to help us."

"Great! Well, then. I'll talk to you in the morning. And listen, Karen, I really am sorry about calling so late. I just didn't realize."

"Forget it, Leslie. Did you enjoy the cabin?"

"How did you know?" Leslie faltered.

"It wasn't hard to guess. If you'd known anyone else in town, you'd have said so before. Therefore you must have been with Rick. It doesn't take a big intellect to figure that out."

Karen's tone was so friendly that it was impossible to take offense.

"The place is beautiful," Leslie said, her knuckles whitening as she clutched the receiver in an effort to keep her voice normal. "And I had a good time."

"Leslie—"

"Don't worry about me, Karen. I'm all right. Rick offered me a chance to try and persuade him about the Star. I didn't succeed, but I enjoyed myself. The weekend's over now, though, and that's the end of that. We have to finish the Helena article. That and doing this series should keep me running till Friday and the auction. I've got to see how that goes. Then it's back to Cleveland."

There was a pause before Karen answered. "All right,

Leslie, I won't ask any questions about you and Rick. Just let me say that if you want to talk, I'm willing to listen."

"Thank you."

"Now, about the series. If you can have the first one ready early in the morning, we might get it in tomorrow's paper."

"Sure, I can," said Leslie. "I'll do it right now. I'm too keyed up to sleep anyway."

"Okay. I'll call you about nine. Good night."

"Good night, Karen." Leslie put the phone back in its cradle and reached for the diary and her notebook. She knew just where to begin—with Maggie's arrival at Last Chance Gulch that summer so long ago.

The next morning Leslie approached the dining room carrying a sheaf of papers. She wanted to try the article out on Paul. By now he should be over most of his anger; he was ordinarily quite an even-tempered man. Pausing at the dining room door, she glanced around. Paul had taken a table by the window. He smiled when he saw her, and Leslie went toward him. "Good morning, Paul."

"Good morning, Leslie." His eyes went over her, and she wondered if he was looking for some visible change. Then his glance moved to the papers in her hand. "Been working?" he asked.

"Sort of." She smiled at him. She did want to stay friendly with Paul. Their working relationship had been a good one. "This is the first of a series of articles on the Star." She settled into her chair. "I talked to Karen about it last night. She's going to get a friend of hers to run them in one of the big papers."

Paul nodded. "Still intent on saving old buildings, huh? I thought maybe you'd forgotten all about stuff like that."

Leslie gave him a sharp look. "Paul, I don't want to fight with you. You know that. So I'll say this and no more. One of the reasons I went with Rick is that I had a chance to talk to him about the Star."

"And did he change his mind?" Paul asked, his sarcasm evident.

"No, he didn't. But I couldn't know that ahead of time." Leslie held his eyes with a firm look. "I'm going to be working on the article now—and on the series for the paper. Rick Donovan is part of my past, a part I don't care to discuss. Is that understood?"

Paul nodded. "I hear you." He looked at her sheepishly. "I didn't mean to fly off the handle like that. I really didn't. Can we be friends again?"

"Yes." Leslie's relief was evident in her voice. "Read the article, won't you, Paul? I tried to make it short and catchy."

"Sure. I'll read it. What are you having for breakfast?"

Leslie shrugged. "The usual, I guess. Bacon and eggs. And tea."

Their order given, Paul turned his attention to the manuscript, while Leslie, nervously sipping tea, tried not to watch him. It was always like this when someone read her work in her presence: her nerves crawled.

Finally Paul raised his head. "I think you're in the wrong part of the business," he said.

Leslie's fingers gripped her cup tightly. "Why?"

"I didn't know you could write stuff like this." He grinned. "Reeking with sentiment."

Leslie's heart fell. "It's that bad?"

"No, Les. Actually it's very good, especially the part about Maggie."

"Those are Maggie's words," Leslie said, relief flooding over her.

He shook his head. "That's good, too, but I liked the part describing Maggie—her youth and vitality, her Irish stubbornness and joy. You made her live for me. It was

146

only because of that—because of my feeling for the woman Maggie—that I had any feelings for the Star."

Leslie stared at him thoughtfully. "You know, Paul. I think you're right." She sighed. It would not be enough to print excerpts about the theatre. She would have to let the readers see Maggie's character, and that meant they would also have to know something about her love and the man she gave it to. Leslie's mind raced. If she did not mention his last name. . . . There must have been many miners named Mick in those early days in the Gulch. There would be no way to connect this one to the Donovans. "Yes, I'm sure you're right. Thanks, Paul. You've given me an idea."

Paul shrugged. "You don't need me to give you ideas, Les. You're full of them." He picked up his coffee cup. "So what's on the agenda today?"

"I have to be back in the room by nine. Karen's going to call me. She hopes to get this one in tonight's paper."

Paul nodded. "She—" He stopped suddenly and took a bite of toast. "That sounds good. But, Les, what about Richardson? We're overstaying our time. You know that."

Leslie's expression hardened. "I'm due a lot of vacation. I'll straighten it out with him later. Right now it's the Star I'm thinking of." She paused, staring at him over the rim of her cup. "Right now I wish you were the artist you wanted to be."

"Why?"

"Because if we had a drawing of Maggie, maybe on the stage of the Star . . ."

Paul grinned. "I said I couldn't paint. I didn't say I couldn't draw."

"You mean you can do it?"

"Of course." Paul drained his cup and glanced at his watch. "You'd better get back to take Karen's call. I'll get my sketch pad and pencils and meet you out on the ter-

147

race. You'll have to be the model. You do look like Maggie, don't you?"

"I–I suppose so." Leslie finished her tea and hurried back to get Karen's call.

CHAPTER 9

Leslie's first article, accompanied by Paul's line drawing of Maggie, the Star in outline behind her, appeared on the front page of the paper owned by Karen's friend and was instantly the talk of the town. Calls for help and donations came pouring into the number listed for auction contributions, and with them came requests for more information about "that dancer."

On the second day Leslie included Maggie's meeting with Mick, and Paul did a drawing of a big brawny Irishman in miner's clothes. Looking at it, Leslie felt a moment's sharp pain. Thankfully, the features were not those of Rick Donovan.

By dint of hard work, polishing, and repolishing every word of the framework that surrounded Maggie's words, and by spending long hours answering the volunteer phone, Leslie managed to have little time to think about Rick. She knew she was only temporarily escaping the pain. But it was as though for the moment she had locked it away.

Reading the third day's piece before it went to press, Paul gave her a strange look. "This guy, this Mick, he was real, wasn't he?"

"Of course." Leslie's heart came up in her throat. Could he have guessed the connection?

"What if he still has some relatives around here?

149

They're not going to like having his story splashed around like this. It doesn't do him much credit, you know."

Leslie managed to keep her face calm. "I'm not telling his last name," she said. "There's no way anyone can prove anything."

Paul frowned. "I don't like this, Les. These wealthy people out here have a lot of power. You don't want to mess with them."

Leslie's laugh was nervous. At least he didn't know the extent of the truth. "Let me worry about that. The contributions are pouring in, Paul. Have you seen? I really think we're going to save the Star!"

Paul's frown did not vanish. "I hope so. I'd hate to see you disappointed. But remember, Les, that conglomerate's got more money than you can imagine. They probably bid low to start with. It's a simple thing for them to raise the ante."

"I know." Leslie's voice reflected her concern. "But I've got to keep hoping."

And so the week wore on. The night hours Leslie spent on the next day's article, working until she fell into bed exhausted. The days she spent manning one of the additional phones. Maggie Callahan had caught at the heart of Helena's citizens.

Wednesday's revised article brought still another warning from Paul, its scarcely veiled references to D and D, causing him to raise an alarmed eyebrow. From a "big business with no interest in the state's past," the "corporation," which was how Leslie referred to it, had become "a leviathan intent on gobbling up the city's irreplaceable and priceless treasures."

"Isn't that a little strong?" asked Paul.

Leslie shrugged. "I didn't mention D and D by name. Besides, I think that's an accurate description."

Paul shook his head. "Leslie, Leslie, you're losing your

perspective. D and D is perfectly within its rights. Business always sells to the highest bidder."

Leslie frowned. "That's just the point, Paul. Big business has only one criterion—money. There *are* other ways of valuing something."

"Of course there are, Les. I never said there weren't." Paul looked exasperated. "But you can't expect business to use your measurements. They're in business to make money. That's their whole purpose."

"I don't care," Leslie replied firmly. "That line stands. People—little people—they'll know what I'm talking about. They're always getting eaten up by big business."

Paul sighed. "I could almost believe you were out to commit professional suicide."

"Come on, Paul," Leslie tried to coax him into a better mood. "You worry too much."

"And you don't worry enough." Paul's words were flat. "You're playing Russian roulette with your career, Les. Richardson is no easy nut to crack. If he gets his back up over this, you're in trouble."

Leslie, her nerves on edge, eyed him angrily. "If you're afraid of old Richardson, just go back to Cleveland. I'm not leaving Helena until Saturday. And until then I'm going to do everything I can to save the Star."

Paul sighed and pushed at his hair. "You know I won't run out on you, Les. I'm not leaving until you do. But if you get us both canned—" He grinned suddenly. "I won't promise not to say 'I told you so.' "

Leslie smiled. "All right, Paul. I'll accept that. And thanks for staying."

It was that night that the phone began to shrill as Leslie reached the motel room. Her heart in her mouth, she raced to answer it. "Hello?"

"Miss Jordan?" The voice was deep and masculine, but not Rick's. Disappointment washed over her.

"Yes, speaking."

"This is Peter Perlson, attorney for D and D."

Leslie sat down on the edge of the bed, her legs suddenly weak. "Yes, Mr. Perlson?" She was glad to hear that her voice remained firm even if her legs did not.

"I understand that you are the author of the pieces currently running in the *Tribune.*"

Leslie was determined not to give an inch. "Which pieces are those, Mr. Perlson?"

"The ones on the Star Theatre and that woman."

Leslie felt her anger rising. "Her name was Maggie Callahan, Mr. Perlson. It has appeared in every article."

"Then you are the author?"

"Yes, Mr. Perlson, I am." She said the words proudly. "I see."

The pause was prolonged, and Leslie suspected that it was done so deliberately to intimidate her. She lay back on the bed and waited. Rick needn't think he could set his lawyer on her and make her back off. He needn't think that at all.

Finally the lawyer spoke. "Miss Jordan, I think you should be warned that court action may be taken against you."

Leslie did not try to hide her anger. "For what, Mr. Perlson? There's nothing in my article but the truth."

"Calling one of Helena's leading businesses a 'gobbling leviathan' is hardly the truth."

Leslie's voice hardened. "Isn't it, Mr. Perlson? What would *you* call it?"

"It is called business, Miss Jordan." His voice was rising now.

Leslie heard the anger in it with satisfaction. No one was going to push her around, least of all a Donovan flunky. "That may be so, Mr. Perlson. However, I have made no mention of D and D in my articles."

"All Helena knows that the Star belongs to D and D."

"Then all Helena can draw its own conclusions," Leslie replied sharply. "The Star is a civic treasure, and D and D is doing nothing to save it."

"That is not quite accurate, Miss Jordan."

For a moment she felt hope. "No?"

"No. D and D is quite willing to see the Star sold to the preservation society. But, as I have pointed out, business is business. All your society has to do is match the conglomerate's offer."

"We have done that, Mr. Perlson, only to be told they have upped their offer. Now, if you've nothing more important than this to say to me, I suggest we terminate this conversation. I intend to write what I think about the Star—and about big business."

"Very well, Miss Jordan." The voice was full of warning. "Just remember that you have brought this upon yourself."

Leslie hung up the phone with a hand that trembled. So this was the way the mighty Mr. Donovan operated! Getting his lawyer to threaten her! For a minute she was so angry that she considered putting the whole story in the next article. But common sense won out. Whatever satisfaction it would bring her, it would not help save the Star. No, she would stick to her original plan. Let them see the Star through Maggie's eyes. But she was not going to tone down her remarks about the corruption that wealth could cause. Maggie knew that, had seen it first hand, and it was right to let it be part of the story.

Finally Friday night and the auction arrived. Leslie, dark circles under her eyes, her hands trembling, donned her long rust skirt and a lacy white blouse, an outfit Karen had told her would be appropriate. Reaching into the drawer for her purse, she saw Maggie's diary. For a moment she hesitated. Then she picked up the plastic bag that she kept it in and put the whole thing carefully into her

153

purse. It was like a talisman, that diary, a good luck charm, and she felt better having it with her.

Actually, it was getting to be rather valuable. More than one caller had offered to buy it. Of course, Leslie had turned them all down. She could not give it up. But the article series had been extremely successful. So much so that she had toyed with the idea of beginning a novel. At any rate, she thought, pulling the door shut behind her, the auction should bring in a lot of people. She could scarcely believe the number of items that had been contributed. If just half the people who had said they would be there showed up, the Star would be packed.

As they had arranged, Paul was waiting for her in the lobby. "Well," he said, "the big night is here."

Leslie nodded.

"I made our reservations on the 10:30 flight in the morning." His usually placid features looked strained as he slid into the rental car. "We *are* leaving then, aren't we?"

"Yes, Paul. I said so, didn't I?" She did not want to talk about leaving Montana.

"And we're going regardless of tonight's results?"

Again Leslie nodded. "Yes. Has Karen heard from D and D?" Her heart skipped a beat as she asked, but her voice remained calm.

"Yes. The man the group's been dealing with—a Carter Alpert—is going to be there tonight. He'll have all the figures for us. The conglomerate's latest offer, et cetera."

Leslie smiled. "For us," she repeated. "I think you've finally seen the light."

Paul's grin was mischievous. "They say when you associate with crazy people long enough it rubs off. And between you and Karen—" He shrugged. "I'll still be glad to see the end of this. I never thought anyone could raise such a stink over one old building."

"I'm surprised myself at the response to the articles,"

154

Leslie agreed. "But I think it's because of Maggie. Her story captured the public's heart. And your drawings helped, too."

Paul smiled. "They were only frosting on the cake. It's Maggie's triumph. She was quite a gal, Maggie was. And her great-granddaughter's pretty special, too."

"Thank you, Paul. Oh! Look at the cars!"

The streets around Reeder's Alley were already packed with parked cars, and uniformed police motioned Paul past the turn. "I hope you wore comfortable shoes," he said. "It's going to be quite a hike back."

Leslie's grin was jubilant. "I wouldn't care if it were five miles, Paul. Look what we've done!"

Her jubilation grew as they neared the theatre, where crowds of people were lining up to get in. Leslie and Paul hurried to the side entrance and up to the stage where Karen was busy working.

"Karen," Leslie cried, "it's fabulous. People are coming and coming. The streets are packed."

"We had to walk four blocks," Paul said. "What time are you opening the doors?"

Karen glanced at her watch. "Not for another fifteen minutes. The auction doesn't start till eight and it's only seven fifteen now." She frowned slightly. "Ordinarily we'd let people walk around and look at things first, but with such a crowd . . ." She smiled slightly. "Well, I guess I'll let Mr. Dailey handle that. He's a professional auctioneer, and he'll know what to do."

"Paul says the D and D man will be here." Leslie felt the familiar pain at the thought of Rick, but she pushed it aside.

Karen nodded. "Yes, I know Carter. He'll be here. In fact, he should be here soon. This afternoon he gave me the conglomerate's latest figures." She smiled. "Carter and I went to school together. I know he's sympathetic to our cause."

155

Leslie was about to ask how someone who worked for D and D could be sympathetic when from across the stage came a hearty male voice. "Karen! There you are." And a big blond man came striding toward them and enveloped Karen in a giant hug.

When he released her, she turned to the others with a laugh. "This is Carter Alpert. Leslie Jordan. Paul Anderson."

Alpert shook Paul's hand, then turned to Leslie. "So this is the celebrated Miss Jordan." Shrewd brown eyes gave her the once-over. "You look mild enough."

Leslie flushed. "What do you mean?"

Alpert chuckled. "I'm afraid that down at the office you're seen as some kind of vicious witch. 'Gobbling leviathan.'" The brown eyes sparkled. "You do turn a nice phrase, Miss Jordan. But physically you're a disappointment. Here I was expecting some old hag with a nose a foot long and fangs to match. And instead I find quite a beautiful young woman."

Leslie joined in the laughter with the rest, but inside she was hurting. So that was how Rick thought of her—the enemy, a vicious witch. Probably he had already forgotten their pleasant hours together, the ecstasy of their fusion— if it had been that for him.

"Well," Alpert said, reaching out to shake her hand, "good luck tonight. And in the future." His smile was genial.

Leslie smiled. "Thank you, Mr. Alpert."

"Well, with those parting words, I'm going to find myself a seat before the hordes descend. See you later."

"He's nice," Leslie said as they watched him make his way backstage.

Karen nodded. "We've been friends for a long time."

"What's he doing working for D and D?"

Karen chuckled. "Until you came to town, D and D was considered quite a respectable business."

Leslie tried to smile. "Maybe I got carried away a little." She had not told the others about the attorney's call. The articles were solely her responsibility. "But I didn't write anything that wasn't true."

Paul raised an eyebrow at this but said nothing, and Karen merely smiled and went on arranging the podium for the auctioneer.

Leslie clutched nervously at her purse. "Do you think we'll make enough?"

Karen shook her head. "I don't know, Leslie. These affairs are hard to predict." She turned to Paul. "There are some seats set aside in the orchestra for you. We're putting some of the more prominent people and the antique dealers there." She smiled. "The ones with money. I hope the crowd isn't going to be too noisy. Oh, Leslie, I almost forgot. There's a Mr. Everett looking for you. He called a little while ago."

Leslie stiffened. Was this another D and D attorney?

"He said he's from Denver, and it's imperative he speak with you. So I told him to come down here. He should be here soon."

Leslie let out a sigh of relief. If he was from Denver, he wasn't a messenger from D and D. She would find out whatever he wanted when the man arrived.

"You two better go get your seats," Karen said, "before they open the doors. At a thing like this possession is nine points of the law."

Taking her arm, Paul moved her off toward the stairs and out the door that led to the orchestra pit. There he found the chairs bearing their names.

"That was a good idea," Leslie said, "to put special guests here."

Paul grinned. "I suggested that the society send personal invitations to dealers and collectors. And it seems to have worked. We asked for RSVPs," he added, seating himself beside her. "I think only two or three didn't reply."

As the door opened to let the crowd in, Leslie looked up at the red velvet curtain that hid the stage and Karen from sight. Only a week had passed since that fateful meeting with Rick. A single week. She was dreadfully nervous, and she did not really know why. She had no actual part in the auction, so there was no need for nerves about that.

Turning in her chair, she began to survey the theatre. The crowd, which had just begun to file in, was noisy and exuberant, the hum of voices growing steadily louder. The seats were filling with people of all shapes and sizes. It was a good-natured crowd, and it cheerfully accepted the fact that the pit was cordoned off. Leslie's eyes alighted on a tall dark figure, its back to her, and her heart stopped beating for a moment and jumped up in her throat. But her eyes had deceived her, she knew that almost immediately. It was not Rick Donovan she saw, moving across the row of seats, but someone of approximately the same size and coloring. Until that very moment she did not know that she had hoped to see him there. But the disappointment that brought scalding tears to her eyes and caused her to swallow over the lump in her throat was clear evidence. Some secret part of her had hoped that Rick would be there. And then what, Leslie said to herself disdainfully. Then what had she expected to happen? It should be clear to anyone with any sense that Rick Donovan wasn't going to show his face at a thing like this. Not that he would let public opinion bother him. Leslie did not for a minute believe that. It was only that she and the society's work at preservation were just trifles to him. Quite probably he had forgotten all about her by now. At least, he hadn't thought what she was doing important enough to merit a personal call. He was probably far away at that very moment, enjoying himself and not even thinking of Montana, let alone Leslie Jordan and the Golden Star.

"Les–lie." Paul's voice carried an insistence that warned her she had been daydreaming.

"Yes, Paul?"

"Here's Mr. Everett."

Leslie looked up to meet the twinkling eyes of a jovial little man. "Hello, Mr. Everett."

"Miss Jordan. If I might have a few moments of your time." In spite of his appearance his tone was quite businesslike.

"Of course." Leslie motioned to the chair beside her.

The little man sent a look toward Paul. Paul did not reseat himself but mumbled something about seeing Karen and left.

Leslie looked to the man beside her. "You wanted to see me, Mr. Everett?"

He nodded. "Yes, you are the author of the series that has been featuring the Star?"

Leslie nodded. Could Donovan have sent to Denver for a high-powered attorney? She tensed as she waited.

"And you are the owner of the diary of Maggie Callahan?"

"Yes." Now it was coming, she thought, preparing herself for the worst.

But Mr. Everett merely smiled. "Good. The sole owner?"

Leslie nodded again. Now she was becoming confused. Exactly what did this man want?

"I represent a publishing house—the Denver Press," he said, presenting her with his card. "We are prepared to make you an offer."

"What kind of offer?" Leslie was bewildered.

"We want to publish Maggie Callahan's diary," Mr. Everett said, "in its entirety. We can get it off the press in

159

a hurry and capitalize on the free publicity it's already gotten."

Leslie could hardly believe her ears. "I'm sorry, Mr. Everett. But Maggie's diary is not for sale. I only used it to help save the Golden Star."

Mr. Everett smiled. "An admirable reason, I'm sure. But we are prepared to offer you twenty thousand dollars for all rights to the manuscript. And, of course, the original would be returned to you."

For a moment Leslie was shaken. Twenty thousand dollars! Then she shook her head. "I'm sorry, Mr. Everett, really I am. But I couldn't do that."

Mr. Everett shrugged. "Maggie Callahan has become a name to be recognized even in Denver. The wire service picked up the series and is running it there—and other places. Interest is quite high. It's received a lot of attention."

Leslie stared at him, her mind in chaos.

"Don't give me an answer now," Mr. Everett said. "Mrs. Hooper has kindly given me a seat over there. I'll see you again before I leave. And thank you."

Before she could say any more he was gone.

Leslie stared into space. How strange her life had become! So, people in Denver knew about Maggie Callahan. Twenty thousand dollars! It was incredible.

Just then the red velvet curtains parted to reveal the big, ruddy auctioneer, Mr. Dailey. A hush fell over the theatre as all eyes turned to the stage.

Karen advanced to the microphone, looking very small and fragile in a long black skirt and white shirtwaist. "Good evening, ladies and gentlemen. I want to welcome you to this benefit auction to save the Golden Star. You can see what a beautiful old place it is, and if we succeed in saving it, we plan to start a little theatre group to play here, as well as a museum and gift shop. And now, without further ado I'd like to thank you all for being here and put

160

the evening into the hands of Pat Dailey, who will handle the auction."

Leslie watched spellbound as the hearty-voiced Dailey drew forth what seemed like enormous sums for the most nondescript items. After a short time there was no doubt in her mind that he was the man for the job. His continual patter was enlivened by jokes and humorous comments about particular members of the audience, which sent certain segments of it roaring off into laughter. When Paul joined her some minutes later, they nodded at each other in quiet approval.

Leslie, watching Karen move unobtrusively in the background, was surprised to find, when her friend stepped forward once again, that several hours had already passed. "Ladies and gentlemen," Karen said, "we thank you for your help. We still have a good many items for your collections, but we thought a little intermission might be helpful here. You'll find refreshments in the front lobby. We'll begin again in fifteen minutes. See you then."

"Let's go backstage." Paul stood up. "And see how things are going."

"Sure." Leslie got to her feet. "I'm anxious to see how much we've made. I've been trying to keep a running total in my head, but I kind of lost track."

"Me, too. But it sure looks good."

Following Paul through the crowd, Leslie made her way backstage to where Karen and Carter Alpert stood deep in conversation. The frown on Karen's face did not look good, and Paul and Leslie hurried closer. "What is it, Karen?" Paul asked.

"It's the conglomerate," Karen said. "We met their last offer, but now Carter tells me they've upped it another fifteen thousand." She sighed. "We're not going to get anywhere near that with the stuff that's left."

Carter Alpert's hearty features were set. "They had a man in the crowd," he said. "I recognized him. He must

161

have had a pretty good idea how much you could offer."
He frowned. "He's gone now. After he made his offer, he
left. He knew you couldn't top it." He sighed. "I'm sorry,
Karen. It's too bad you can't raise that extra fifteen. Then
we could close the deal without letting them bid again.
After all, he did tell me that was his final offer."

Karen shook her head. "There's no way we can raise
that kind of money tonight, Carter. I guess we've been
beaten."

"Not yet." Leslie heard her own voice with surprise.
"Not yet. Mr. Alpert, will you stay here a little longer?"

"Of course."

"Leslie, I know you want to help, but there's nothing
more to do. They've won."

Leslie shook her head vehemently. "No, Karen, they
haven't. Just wait. Please!"

Three pairs of eyes stared at her with unconcealed concern, but Karen replied, "All right, Leslie. We'll wait."

Leslie turned and hurried back toward the pit. If only
Mr. Everett was still there. She peered out over the crowd,
trying to find him. She reached the orchestra pit and
glanced hurriedly around. She had to find him, and find
him now. But there were so many people milling about
that it was hard to see. Then the crowd in front of her
opened slightly, and she spied him just settling back into
his seat. Clutching her purse, she hurried toward him.
"Mr. Everett—"

"Miss Jordan. I was just looking for you. Have you
made up your mind?"

"I—there are some things I need to ask."

"Of course." He patted the empty seat beside him. "Sit
down. I'll be glad to answer any questions."

Leslie dropped into the chair. "You want to print the
whole diary?"

"Yes. Just as it is."

"Could you possibly delete something?"

Mr. Everett looked bewildered. "I don't understand."

"The man who was Maggie's . . . lover. . . ." Leslie's tongue stumbled over the word. "He has descendants in the city. Prominent people. I wouldn't want them to get adverse publicity."

Mr. Everett frowned. "Hmmmm. That puts a new light on the matter. The company wouldn't want to cause problems for anyone—including ourselves." His tight smile showed that he had correctly translated the word "prominent." "I don't see why we couldn't leave Mick's last name out. Yes, we can do that."

Leslie took a deep breath. "Then I have only one more stipulation."

Mr. Everett looked expectant.

"I have to have the money tonight."

The little man looked startled. "Tonight?"

Leslie leaned closer. "You see, we need it to save the Star. That's why I'm agreeing to the sale. But if we don't have it tonight, we'll lose the theatre. And then I won't be willing to sell at all."

"You mean you're going to donate the twenty thousand to save this theatre?" Mr. Everett's eyes bugged slightly.

"Yes. Can I have it tonight?" Leslie asked impatiently. "Now?"

Mr. Everett looked slightly stunned. "Well, this is certainly unorthodox, to say the least. But I was empowered to reach an agreement with you." Suddenly he smiled broadly. "Miss Jordan, it's a deal." He fumbled in his pocket. "Now, if you'll wait just a moment, I'll give you a check to close the deal officially."

Leslie, her knuckles white as she gripped the purse that held Maggie's precious diary, sighed deeply. Was she wrong to do this to Maggie, to give away her deepest secrets? And yet Maggie had loved this place, loved it with a deep, abiding affection. She would have fought to save it. And there was nothing shameful about Maggie's life—or her love. She had lived up to her principles.

"Here you are, Miss Jordan. This check closes the deal. I'll have the official contract in the morning."

Leslie took the check. "Please make your visit early," she said. "We're leaving for the airport at 9:30."

"Of course." He looked at her expectantly. "You will have the diary ready then?"

Leslie nodded. "You're sure I can have the original back?"

"Of course, Miss Jordan. Don't you worry now. Denver Press is quite a reputable firm. Ask your friends. We'll take good care of Maggie's diary and return it to you. You'll have to put your permanent address on the contract."

"Yes, I will. Thank you, Mr. Everett."

"Thank you, Miss Jordan. This book is going to go places. I feel it in my bones."

As she made her way back through the moving crowd, Leslie tried to feel elation. The Star would be saved. Maggie's diary would still be hers. And she had managed the deal so as not to harm Rick's reputation. Yet she could feel no joy at all. Just a sort of deadness. For tomorrow she would leave the Star and Montana behind her. And although common sense told her that this was the way it had originally been planned, she felt as Maggie had—that she was leaving behind both the man and the land that she loved.

The little group was still standing where she had left them, their faces reflecting their concern. Paul was the first to see her coming. "Here's Leslie now."

With a trembling hand she offered the check to Karen. "Here, this should give us enough."

Karen looked at the figures, then looked again. "Leslie!" Her voice was incredulous. "Twenty thousand dollars! You can't!"

"Yes, I can." Conscious that Paul and Carter Alpert were staring at her in surprise, she continued. "I sold Maggie's diary." Sudden anxiety struck her. "To the Denver Press. It's reputable, isn't it?"

Karen nodded. "Yes, of course. But twenty thousand dollars. Leslie, you can't give that away."

"Yes, I can. That's the only reason I sold it—to save the Star. Will we have enough?"

Karen nodded. "Yes, we will. But—"

"Please, Karen, make the deal now. Before the conglomerate makes another offer. That's why I insisted on getting it tonight."

Karen turned to Carter Alpert. "Can we do that?"

"Sure thing. They told me that was their last offer. You just need to top it by a dollar."

Karen seemed in a state of shock. "I can't believe this. I can't believe we're really going to win."

"Wonder about it later," said Alpert dryly. "Miss Jordan is right. I'm fully within my instructions to close the deal now, Karen. But if the conglomerate hears about this, they're apt to up the bid again."

Paul, who had stood silent through all of this, now approached Leslie and whispered urgently. "Les, stop and think. Twenty thousand! You can't just throw that away."

Leslie faced him squarely. "I know you're trying to help me, Paul. And I know that you can't really understand my feelings for this place. But this is something I *want* to do, *have* to do. And that's all there is to it."

Paul nodded, acknowledging defeat, but his eyes were still rebellious, and she knew that he thought her actions strange in the extreme, that her stay in this country had rearranged her values, and in a very wrong way. But as she watched Karen and Alpert exchange the papers that finalized the sale, she knew she had done the right thing, the thing Maggie would have wanted done. That much she felt deeply. She was unable to stretch her mind much beyond

165

the present moment; she could not visualize the refurbished Star, its stage bright with theatrical productions.

Her mind was just too tired. It was enough simply to know that the Star was safe.

She turned to Paul. "Let's go back to our seats. They'll be resuming the auction again."

The rest of the items were speedily auctioned off. Then Karen came to the mike again. "Ladies and gentlemen, I'm sure you would like to share our good news. Because of your generosity . . . and the donation of a large sum by a friend of the theatre . . . the Star has been saved! We are in the process now of concluding the transaction. As Montanans we can be proud that we have saved another important part of our cultural heritage. But this time we had outside help. You all know the name of Maggie Callahan —that courageous woman who worked in this theatre." A great roar went up from the audience. "But you don't know Maggie's great-granddaughter, Leslie Jordan. It was Leslie who in sharing Maggie's story with us helped us to see the Star through other eyes. And it was Leslie's contribution—the whole profit from the sale of Maggie's diary —which has made our enterprise a success. I want you to meet Leslie Jordan."

With Karen's extended hand pointing to her and Paul whispering insistently in her ear, Leslie had no choice but to rise and acknowledge the thunderous applause. Her face frozen into a stiff smile, she did so. How Maggie would have loved that applause, she thought as she bowed in each direction in turn. *It's yours anyway, Maggie,* she said silently. *You saved the Star.*

She accompanied Paul to the impromptu party thrown to celebrate their triumph. She ate and drank, danced and laughed, with all the rest, but she could not feel the elation that she so successfully pretended. And when she was finally alone in her motel room, she stripped off her clothes and fell across the bed.

Tomorrow she would be back in Cleveland. Montana and everything that had happened here would be nothing but a memory, no more real to her, perhaps even less real, than the events in Maggie's diary. She would never see Rick Donovan again. Nor, most likely, Montana. For to return here would be to resurrect memories better left buried under the debris of time. If ever time was able to bury them.

She got to her feet in the darkness and walked across to pull open the curtains. The Montana sky was a clear midnight blue; hundreds of stars sparkled in it like diamonds on a field of velvet. Hot tears burned in Leslie's eyes. She loved this country of extremes, loved it with an affection that would never be eradicated. But, like Maggie, she would have to leave it behind.

Suddenly cold, Leslie turned and stumbled back to the bed. Her mind, which she had succeeded in keeping busy with work on the Star, was now insisting that she think of the man she loved. Lying there in the summer darkness, she saw him again against her closed eyelids—tall, dark, arrogant. Like the god they had pretended he was. And yet, in spite of the polished shell he presented to the world, and the sophisticated playboy role that he played, Leslie knew that inside was a man with finer feelings, a man capable of tenderness, of caring. Of love even—if only he would give himself a chance. But she had not been able to reach him. And she would not see him again.

He would probably think of her briefly when he heard of the sale of the diary, and then she would fade from his memory again. Would he even bother to buy a copy? she wondered. And if he did, would he know enough to recognize his great-grandfather?

On the bed Leslie suddenly froze. Mr. Everett had agreed to delete Mick's last name, but there were other clues to his identity: the year of Maggie's arrival, the name of the mine, the date of his marriage, the name of the society bride. A dozen things. Any competent person could easily search out Mick's last name. Oh, why hadn't she thought of that before?

Again Leslie rose and began to pace the floor. In the heat of the moment, in her anxiety to save the theatre, she had not considered all the details. And now it was too late. She could not back down on the deal. And all the clues to Mick's identity could not be camouflaged. The dates and his first name were enough for any diligent researcher to ascertain, and they had already appeared in the articles.

Suddenly she stopped her pacing and turned to the writing desk. She could not go away letting Rick think she had done this thing on purpose, some kind of revenge on him. She would write him a letter, explaining exactly what had happened. He might believe it, and at least she would have done what she could. She took out pen and paper.

The wastebasket was full, and the hands of the clock stood at three before Leslie had a satisfactory letter before her. She read through it once more and nodded wearily. Everything was there, as clear as she could make it. She put her signature on the bottom and slipped it into an envelope. A quick call to the desk assured her that it could be delivered to the Donovan Building the first thing in the morning.

Leslie set her traveling alarm and crawled wearily between the sheets. Perhaps now she could sleep. And hopefully her dreams would not, as they had been the past nights, be filled with memory images of Rick: of his strong, hard body; of his dark, handsome features; and worst of all, of the hurt she had seen hiding in those blue eyes.

CHAPTER 10

Leslie's first action when she awoke the next morning was to call the desk and arrange for the early delivery of her letter to Rick. She could not leave Montana, she told herself, with any sense of peace until she knew that the letter was on its way. It was a sort of symbol to her, marking the end to their relationship. It would, she hoped, erase some of her sense of being left dangling in the middle of something very important.

As she placed the rough draft of her *Vacations Today* article in her bag, she smiled. Richardson would have a fit if he knew how much time she'd spent on that series for the *Tribune*. But she was going to take this week as vacation and pay the bill for the expenses herself. She had vacation time coming, and if Richardson was upset, well, right now she couldn't care less.

She had all her cases packed when a knock on the door announced Mr. Everett. Leslie let him in.

"You're an early riser, I see." He took in the neat appearance of the room. "Here's our contract. I'm sure you'd like to read it through."

Leslie took it. "Sit down, Mr. Everett. It won't take me long."

Minutes later she raised her head. "It seems very straightforward to me except that I don't understand this clause about the royalties."

"That's our standard package," said Mr. Everett. "Six

169

percent on the first hundred thousand copies. Eight on the next."

"Yes, I see that. But the twenty thousand?"

"That was an advance against royalties, Miss Jordan. Frankly, we made it that large so as to get your quick consent. It's nonrefundable, however, so you needn't worry about that. Actually we're quite confident the diary will sell well. The way it came to light will help. And your donation to the society. Great human interest." He smiled. "In fact, we've already made arrangements with Mrs. Hooper to stock the theatre bookstore she plans. They may even put on a production that recounts how the Star was saved. And include a copy of the diary with each benefit ticket. We also have permission from the *Tribune* to run your series as an introduction. I suppose you have no objection to that."

Leslie shook her head. "None at all. This whole thing is beyond me, Mr. Everett. Just let me sign the contract."

"Don't worry, Miss Jordan. The diary will be returned to you. You saw that stipulation? And the last name of the prominent family will be deleted."

Leslie nodded and put her signature in the indicated space. "Thank you, Mr. Everett. You've been a godsend."

The little man laughed heartily. "Thank *you*. Be sure to put your Cleveland address on the contract. We'll be in touch with you. Talk shows and the like. Incidentally, though the contract doesn't mention it, we'd very much like to have first look at any novels you might do in the future."

Leslie, still stunned by the idea of talk shows, could only stare at him.

Mr. Everett chuckled. "I don't believe you realize it, Miss Jordan, but you are quite a celebrity."

"Me?" Leslie's shock was evident.

"Yes. Wire services all over the West have picked up the

story of your fight to save Maggie's theatre. Frankly, I'm surprised that other publishers haven't gotten to you."

For the first time in the last hour Leslie smiled. "I'm afraid I wasn't too accessible, Mr. Everett. And, anyway, I'm glad they didn't. I like dealing with you."

Mr. Everett's eyes twinkled. "I trust it will be profitable for both of us, though I suppose you will have to wait some time for yours." He shook his head. "I must admit that I was quite surprised to have you donate the whole amount of the advance. Such philanthropy is astounding."

Leslie shrugged. "It's what Maggie would have wanted. She loved the Star."

Mr. Everett put the contract in his briefcase. "I wish you a pleasant flight. Although, I am rather surprised that you're leaving so soon. You have such an evident love for the West."

Leslie managed a small smile. "I'm a working woman, Mr. Everett. And aʳ much as I love Montana, my job is not here."

"I understand. Well, Miss Jordan, I know you have things to do. I'll be on my way." He rose and extended his hand. "Good luck to you wherever you are. We'll be in touch."

As she closed the door behind his retreating figure Leslie looked down at a hand that trembled. So much had happened in the last week. She had seen the Montana of her dreams. She had held twenty thousand dollars in her hand and given it away. And she had found—and lost—a man she loved.

Absently she checked all the drawers, the bathroom shelves, the closet. Imagine Leslie Jordan on a talk show . . . imagine *her* words being used to introduce Maggie's story to thousands of people.

She found nothing that hadn't been packed, and satisfied on that score, made her way to the dining room to meet Paul for breakfast.

171

* * *

Promptly at 9:30 the rented car pulled away from the motel. Leslie did not look back. There was no point to it.

As he eased the car through the traffic Paul spoke, "Are you sure you're all right, Les? You've hardly said a word."

Leslie managed a small smile. "It's just aftereffects, I guess. A kind of letdown after all the excitement."

Paul did not return the smile. "I think you ought to see a doctor as soon as we get home. You're awfully pale, and you're getting dark circles under your eyes."

"I'll be all right, Paul. Really I will. I'm just tired. A little rest and I'll be good as new." She dared not look at him, for her throat was tightening up on her. Fatigue really had nothing to do with the feelings she was enduring. They were feelings concerned with leaving Montana —and Rick Donovan—behind her.

She must think of something else, Leslie told herself as she stared unseeing at the passing streets. There would be plenty of time for grief later, years and years for recalling each word, each touch, each look, that was stored away in her aching heart. But for now she must put all that aside. She had done enough to hurt Paul on this trip, unintentional though it had been; she would not burden him with a weepy, hysterical woman for the flight home. She set her chin and began to count the trees along the sidewalk. Anything to occupy her mind.

They had driven for perhaps ten minutes when the sudden sound of a siren caused Leslie to turn. "Is it a fire?" she asked Paul.

"I don't think so. A cop just went past me, then did a U turn and put on his siren. I don't know who he wants. I didn't see anyone doing anything." As he spoke he eased the car over to the curb. "We'll just get out of his way."

But to their surprise the patrol car did not go by; instead, it pulled to a stop behind them.

Paul looked at Leslie. "I wasn't even doing the speed

172

limit. I don't understand." He turned to the window as the officer approached.

"Paul Anderson? Leslie Jordan?"

"Yes."

"Follow me."

"But, Officer, we have a plane to catch."

The policeman was young and polite, but he was obviously used to respect. "Look, lady. I don't know anything about that. If you miss your plane, you just get another. But if you don't come with me—" He shook his head. "Then you're apt to be in a lot of trouble. Got it?"

"Got it," Paul said, sending Leslie a warning look. "We'll follow you."

"Good."

As they pulled back into traffic, Paul sticking close behind the patrol car, Leslie frowned. "What on earth is going on?"

Paul shrugged. "Your guess is as good as mine. But one thing I learned early. Never argue with a cop. And most especially in a strange town."

Leslie shook her head. "I just don't understand it."

Paul's grin was only slightly strained. "Don't bother to try. Someone will explain soon enough. Very soon, it looks like," he added as the police car pulled to a halt, and he followed suit.

Leslie, peering out the window, gasped. "That's the Donovan Building!"

Again the officer appeared at the window. "Just leave the keys. I'll see that it gets parked. You can take Miss Jordan up. Mr. Donovan is waiting."

"Yes, Officer." Paul slid out of the seat and came around to open the door for Leslie. The warning in his eyes kept her silent until they were inside the lobby door. Then her indignation could no longer be contained.

"Paul! I don't want to see Rick Donovan."

Paul shrugged. "I'm afraid that means very little, Les.

It's apparent the man has clout. A lot of it. If he wants to see you, he's going to see you. And that's that."

"But, Paul—"

"Leslie." Paul's patience was strained; she could see that. "I didn't think you should get mixed up with this guy in the first place, but you did. Now, just go see what he wants so we can leave. I've got things to do at home."

Leslie gave in. She would have to face Rick. That much seemed clear. "You might as well come up and sit in the great man's waiting room," she said bitterly. "You're entitled to that much."

Paul stepped into the elevator beside her. "You never take my advice," he said, "but I'm giving it anyway. Donovan has power, Les. Bushels of it. Don't provoke him. Men with power can be very destructive."

Leslie nodded, the lump in her throat making her unable to reply.

As they stepped out into the plushly decorated waiting room Paul whistled softly under his breath. "Class."

The clipped British tones of the secretary carried across the room: "Mr. Donovan will see you in his office, Miss Jordan."

"Thank you." With a last look at Paul, Leslie advanced to the door behind which Rick Donovan waited. Part of her longed to see him, to take one last look at the man she loved. But another part insisted that the pain would be too great.

Leslie took a deep breath and opened the door. The big windows across the room flooded it with Montana sunshine. Outlined against them, his back to her, stood the figure of a tall, lean man. Leslie's heart rose up in her throat as she looked at him, and for a moment her legs wouldn't move. Then she forced herself to step closer. "Mr. Donovan . . ." she began.

He turned to face her as she spoke, but the brilliant light behind him blinded her, and his face was all in shadow.

174

Leslie took another deep breath and began again. "Mr. Donovan, what do you mean by having me–us–stopped like common criminals?"

"I mean to see you," he replied, his voice even, his face still shadowed.

"I can't imagine why you should want to see me." She forced herself to face him steadily.

"I want to talk to you."

"I don't believe we have anything to discuss." She said the words sharply, prompted by the pain of seeing him like this.

"Oh, no?" His tone was steely, and remembering that other occasion in his office, she quivered with sudden fright.

"What are you talking about?"

"I'm talking about this letter that I found waiting for me . . . a letter in which I am informed that not only have you obtained your heart's desire, the Golden Star Theatre —and by somewhat questionable means, I might add— but you have sold the rights to your great-grandmother's diary, which *now* you tell me holds information detrimental to the reputation of my family. I believe I have the right to discuss this matter with you."

Leslie's knees were beginning to get weak. "You have no right to have me stopped like that."

"Was the police officer discourteous?" His voice was hard.

"No. But he had his orders. And he carried them out."

"Of course. Power has its uses. You should know that, Leslie."

Her heart jumped at the sound of her name on his lips, and she started nervously as he stepped around the desk and came toward her.

"Sit down, Leslie. I want to talk."

"I have a plane to catch."

"I'll see that you get a flight later. Sit down."

175

Leslie settled into a chair. "Another of the uses of power," she said harshly.

He nodded. "Of course." He sank into a chair himself, but as his back was still to the sun, she found it difficult to make out the expression on his face.

"Now, Leslie. Let's talk about your letter."

"What about it?" She hated the quiver in her voice, but she couldn't control it.

"First, why did you write it?"

Leslie clasped her hands nervously in her lap. "I thought you deserved an explanation. When I sold the diary, I was very upset, not thinking particularly straight. I thought about the Donovan name being in it. I asked that it be deleted. But it wasn't until later that I realized that wouldn't be enough. The diary has dates and other names—that of the mine, and the woman Mick married. It wouldn't take a competent researcher long to have the whole story." She watched his features, but they remained set.

"But why tell me?" he asked. "Why not let the storm hit me unawares?"

Leslie sat erect. "I don't believe you understand me very well, Mr. Donovan. I couldn't cancel the sale. It had already been announced. But I could give you some forewarning. And my apologies."

"I see." His voice was cold. "I must add that the story of your giving the entire twenty thousand to the preservation society was a nice touch. It was clever of you and Karen to work that out."

Leslie stared at him. "What do you mean?"

"I mean that I'm not fool enough to believe that anyone gives away twenty grand, especially not anyone in your financial bracket."

"You are a fool, Rick Donovan." Leslie spat the words out. "The 'story' you heard was the truth. I gave every

176

cent of that advance to the society. And if you don't believe me—well, that's just too bad!"

She started to rise. "Just a minute, Miss Jordan. I'm not through."

Angrily Leslie fell back into the chair. She longed to storm out, slamming the door behind her. But that would be as futile as it was childish. Rick had all the power here. She would have to wait until he allowed her to leave. "All right, what else?"

"I find your behavior puzzling," he said. "And I would like an explanation."

"Of what?" Leslie did not bother to hide her annoyance.

"You had the diary when you first arrived?"

"Yes."

"But you didn't tell me it had the Donovan name in it."

"Why should I?"

"It would have made far better sense to offer me the diary in exchange for letting your group have the theatre at their price."

For a moment Leslie stared at him, her face going a pasty white. "You mean—blackmail you?"

He shrugged. "You might call it that. It surely would have simplified matters."

"You're crazy," Leslie muttered. "I couldn't—blackmail anyone."

"And now you're in a great deal of trouble."

"H–how?" Her throat had gone dry. He meant business.

"The articles in the *Tribune* got nationwide attention. So will the publication of this diary. Everett will see to that. D and D is going to get some very bad press when the truth gets out."

Leslie swallowed. "I'm sorry about that. I really am. But I can't help it." She tried to read his expression but could not.

"I'm afraid that's not good enough, Leslie. You'll have to make reparation."

"What are you talking about?" Fear made her voice quiver.

"There is one way to counteract all the bad publicity we're going to get, one thing you can do."

"I'll do anything I can," she replied. "But I don't see—"

"Good. We'll be married next week then."

For a moment the room seemed to spin madly around Leslie, and she thought perhaps her senses had betrayed her. "You–you can't mean that," she faltered.

"I never say anything I don't mean," he replied, his voice flat. "There is only one way to counteract the talk: the descendants of Maggie and Mick get together. Lo, love blooms, and they marry. A beautiful ending to the old story."

Leslie, shaken to the very core of her being, stared at him. "But marriage—that's impossible."

"I don't see why." His voice remained flat and emotionless, and his expression did not change. "In one area we are quite compatible."

"There's more to marriage than that! I–I'm not suitable," she cried angrily.

"You're not from one of the East's—or the West's—best families," he said dryly. "But under the circumstances that's just as well."

"The whole thing is impossible," she cried, trying to hold on to the control she felt slipping away from her.

"I don't require a society wife," he said evenly. "You're in good health. Your family background is sound enough."

"I'm afraid you don't understand, Mr. Donovan." Leslie choked back the tears. "I don't care how much money you have. Or how much power. Or what you think of my background. Or anything else! I can't marry you. A loveless marriage is—unthinkable for me." She could no long-

178

er keep back the tears, and she struggled to her feet and turned blindly toward the door.

As that other time, he was there before her, his hands reaching out to grab her upper arms. "You'll have to marry me, Leslie There's no other way."

She could not see him clearly because of the tears coursing down her cheeks. "I—can't. Let—me—go. Marriage without love! I can't!"

She was almost completely blinded by her tears, but as he drew her swiftly into his arms, she struck out. "No!" It seemed to her distracted senses that if he kissed her now, after the insult of such a degrading proposal, she would hate him forever.

But his arms showed her no mercy, crushing her against his chest and holding her there. She struggled, trying to free her hands to strike at him, trying to kick at him. But he might as well have been a rock for all the harm her efforts did him.

And then, when she had no more energy left to fight, he used one hand to raise her lips to his. She tasted the salt of her own tears. She tried to resist him, but she was weakened by her own longing, appalled by the knowledge that she loved him so much that for one terrible moment she had actually considered accepting his proposal, considered a marriage that would inevitably become a living hell.

To her surprise his lips did not attack hers brutally and savagely, wresting acquiescence from her. Instead they moved softly, persuasively, in a way that could only be called tender. She felt her resistance crumbling. Her body, which had so long desired the feel of his, automatically molded itself against him and her lips, which she had tried to keep firm and unyielding, softened and surrendered under his. When finally he released her mouth and looked down at her, her knees quivered with weakness.

"We have passion," he said softly. "Couldn't you *learn* to love me?"

Deeply shaken by her feelings, Leslie did not think before she replied. "That isn't the problem," she whispered against his shoulder. "You don't love *me.*" The words ended with a jerky sob.

"Leslie, look up at me. Please."

The note of pleading in his voice was so unusual that she raised her eyes to his face. But she could not fathom the expression she found there.

"Now, Leslie, I want you to listen to me. Listen carefully." As she started to protest, he put a finger on her lips. "Wait. Hear me out. You owe me that much. Don't you?" His blue eyes looked down seriously into hers.

"Yes, but—"

"No buts, Leslie. Just listen. The same evening I left you at the motel, I flew out of Montana. When I walked away from you, I got the strangest feeling inside. I didn't like it. It was like what I felt earlier in the day when you mentioned other men." He closed his eyes as though remembering. "So I went to London, Paris, Cannes."

Leslie's head was spinning, but her body, still leaning against his, felt comfortably at peace.

"I had a lot of women."

She stiffened and tried to pull away, but his arms kept her imprisoned. "I did all the things I used to do. All of them and more. But nothing worked. I still had this strange feeling—like something was wrong with me. Like I'd lost part of myself." He paused as though looking for words, and Leslie, his body so close to her own, could only wait.

"Finally I came back to Helena. I got in early this morning and came straight to the office. Alpert had left a report about the Star. It mentioned your donation." His smile was sheepish. "It never occurred to me that you might *really* give a donation like that."

She opened her mouth, and he kissed it briefly, sending tremors down her spine. "I know. I was wrong. Then your letter arrived, telling me about the diary and the rest. And that you were leaving."

The arms around her tightened till she wondered if she'd be able to breathe. "I had to stop you," he went on. "I had to see you again. I called the motel; you were already gone. So I called the police. I know, I know, it was wrong. But I was frantic. I couldn't let you leave like that."

The idea of a frantic Rick Donovan was so unusual to Leslie that for a moment she missed what he was saying.

"I had to see you again. Get this insanity out of my system."

"Insanity?" She forgot her promise to listen.

"Yes. This feeling that without you I'm not complete."

Leslie stared at him. She felt she must be dreaming. He couldn't be saying what she thought he was saying. He couldn't be having feelings so like her own. That was impossible.

For long moments she stared at him, the silence between them lengthening. His body was hard against hers, his breath warm on her forehead. His eyes held cloudy shadows. Finally Leslie spoke. "And so to rid yourself of this insanity you proposed marriage? Isn't that a rather drastic solution."

He grinned that little boy grin she loved. "I didn't think of it till I saw you." His face sobered. "I thought seeing you would erase some kind of false image I had of you."

"And did it?" The words were a mere whisper.

He shook his head, one hand reaching up to caress her wet cheek. "No. I took one look at you and knew I was a goner."

Leslie let out a deep breath, leaning her cheek against his hand. "But why did you ask me like that? You knew. I told you. I could never marry without love."

With his thumb he wiped away a tear. "You told me a lot of things." He sighed and an expression of sadness clouded his face. "I'm afraid I didn't believe most of them. I'd lost the ability to believe, Leslie. Can you understand that?"

She nodded. "Yes, I think so."

He dropped a kiss on her forehead. "I want to marry you, Leslie. I don't really give a damn about the press. You know that, don't you?"

His tone carried anxiety. "The Donovans have had a lot of bad publicity. It never hurt us." His expression was strained. "You do believe me, don't you, Leslie? You don't think I'm lying?"

She shook her head. "I can't imagine you being afraid of anything," she said softly. "But that proposal! You tried to browbeat me."

His grin was sheepish. "I have some bad habits. I'm afraid I'm used to having my own way. Anyhow, it might have worked."

Leslie shook her head firmly. "Bullying never works with me. Never."

"I'll remember that." He hugged her close. "What kind of wedding do you want?"

"Wedding?" Leslie's heart rose up in her throat. This all seemed unreal.

"Wedding," he repeated. "You are going to marry me, aren't you?" The hand that was caressing her back paused momentarily.

"Rick—I don't know." Faced with the chance of having her dream, Leslie hesitated. "It's so soon. We hardly know each other. Maybe we should wait. Be sure."

He shook his head. "We'll wait if you say so, Leslie. But *I'm* sure. I've never felt this way about anyone." His lips brushed her forehead, and a tremor ran down her spine. "Never."

She knew then why she had held back. But could she

ask him outright? She took another tack. "Children?" she stammered.

"Of course," he replied. "But not right away. I want you to myself for a while." He grinned. "There is one thing, Leslie. One thing that's not perfect about you."

"Yes?"

"Your penchant for preservation societies. I want a wife, not a crusader."

She sensed the old pain behind the light words, and her tone was completely serious. "I saved the Star, Rick. And I might want to help with other projects, but never at the expense of our relationship. Or our children."

"Good." His sigh of relief was a big one. "Now, how long do we have to wait?"

"I don't know. I want to be sure."

"Sure of what, Leslie? You already know what a good thing we have. Why waste any more time?"

She knew then that she would have to risk it. "I—" She hid her face against his shoulder. "I need the words, Rick. Say them for me."

"What words?"

She looked at him, tears filling her eyes. "Tell me—tell me how you feel about me."

He looked startled. "You drive me crazy. When I'm away from you, I can't think of anything else. I want to marry you. I want to share my life with you. What more could you want?"

Leslie looked into the eyes so close to her own. "I want the words you won't say." Her voice was just a whisper in the quiet room. "I need those words, Rick."

He hesitated and as she watched his eyes clouded and then cleared again. "I—" He stopped.

"Have you ever said them?" she asked softly, dreading his answer, yet knowing she had to ask.

His features were set and hard, his voice clipped. "Once.

Long ago." His grip on her tightened. "They're only words, Leslie. You know how I feel. You have *me*."

She shook her head, knowing instinctively what she must do. "No, Rick. They're more than words. To me. And to you." She saw the pain in his face but pressed on. "You'll never be free of her, until you can say them again. If not to me, then to someone else."

He frowned. "There'll never be anyone else," he said.

"Then give me the words, Rick, please." Her heart was pounding with fear. If he could not say them, if he could not tell her he loved her, then she could not enter whole-heartedly into their marriage. She could not do it without those precious words.

"Leslie." He seemed to be having a battle with himself. "I swore never to say them to a woman again."

Tears filled her eyes as she gazed up at him. "I'm sorry, Rick." She choked on the words. She hid her face in his shoulder, sobs shaking her slender frame.

"God, Leslie, don't! Don't cry like that! I love you. . . ." He paused, almost as startled by the words as she was. "Leslie," he cried, his voice triumphant. "I said it! I love you! I love you!"

"Oh, Rick!" Gazing up into his joyful face, she smiled through her tears. "Now I know. I'll marry you any time you say."

He lifted her off her feet in an exuberant hug.

"Oh, Leslie, you can't imagine how I felt, thinking you were gone, thinking I'd never see you again."

"Can't I?" she whispered. Tentatively she reached up to touch his cheek with tender fingers. "Oh, darling, I can't believe this is true."

"You'd better believe it," he said. "You've only got three days to get used to the idea of being Mrs. Rick Donovan."

"Three days?"

"I think that's what it takes." He smiled down at her.

"Unless you want an absolutely stupendous wedding. That might take four days."

Leslie felt numb. "It's all so fast. I can hardly think. I know I want a gown. I only plan to do this once, you know."

Rick nodded. "Me, too. Who do you want to stand up with us?"

"I don't know anyone here."

"There's Karen."

Leslie hesitated. "But she . . ."

"Cared for me once?"

"Yes."

"I think she's over that now. And what about your friend Paul? Would he be our best man? Or is he apt to punch me in the nose?"

Leslie grinned uneasily. "I don't know. Oh!"

"What is it?"

"Paul! He's waiting out there. By now he'll be a nervous wreck."

Rick brushed her lips with his. "Then let's go make him unnervous." He grinned. "I think you might be in for a little surprise." And taking her hand in his, he opened the outer door.

Leslie gasped. Across the room sat Paul, and beside him, their heads close together, sat Karen Hooper.

"Hello, Leslie." Karen's look took in Rick's arm possessively around her waist.

"Hello, Karen." Leslie was still too surprised to say much.

Paul grinned. "Well, I guess your differences with Mr. Donovan have been settled."

Leslie nodded. "But, Karen, what are you doing here?"

"Rick called me. And when I heard his story, I asked him to send a car for me." She smiled. "My good-bye to Paul last night was not very satisfactory, and I wanted to see him again."

Leslie was bewildered. "I don't think I understand."

Rick squeezed her close against him. "It's like this, love: While we've been wandering around in our separate little hells, Karen and Paul have been building a heaven together. Except that his concern for you has kept them from reaching out for it."

"And when he discovered how Rick felt about you—" Karen grinned. "Then he popped the question to me."

"Really?" Leslie's eyes sparkled. "Oh, Karen, that's terrific." She turned. "Paul, I'm so happy for you."

"And me for you, Les." Paul's smile was genuine.

Leslie turned to Rick, her arm stealing around his waist. "I think it's all right to ask them," she said.

Rick returned the smile. "I thought it would be. Leslie and I want you to stand up with us. Probably on Thursday. We'll discuss the details later." He nodded to Paul. "If I were you, I'd take Karen home now. I'll see that Leslie gets back to the motel. Later." Grinning brashly, he added, "Much later," and pulled her into the office, closing the door softly behind them.

Dell Bestsellers

From the author of *Evergreen*

RANDOM WINDS

by
BELVA PLAIN

From a quiet village in upstate New York to elegant house parties in the English countryside…from the bedsides of the rural poor to the frenetic emergency room of a Manhattan hospital…from war-torn London to luxurious lovers' hideaways on the Riviera, here is the unforgettable story of three generations of doctors—and of a love no human force could surpress.

A Dell Book $3.50   (17158-X)

The unforgettable saga of a
magnificent family

IN JOY AND IN SORROW

by

JOAN JOSEPH

They were the wealthiest Jewish family in Portugal, masters of
Europe's largest shipping empire. Forced to flee the scourge of
the Inquisition that reduced their proud heritage to ashes, they
crossed the ocean in a perilous voyage. Led by a courageous,
beautiful woman, they would defy fate to seize a forbidden
dream of love.

A Dell Book   **$3.50**   **(14367-5)**

The second volume in the
spectacular Heiress series

The Cornish Heiress

by Roberta Gellis
bestselling author of
The English Heiress

Meg Devoran—by night the flame-haired smuggler, Red Meg.
Hunted and lusted after by many, she was loved by one man
alone...

Philip St. Eyre—his hunger for adventure led him on a
desperate mission into the heart of Napoleon's France.

From midnight trysts in secret smugglers' caves to wild
abandon in enemy lands, they pursued their entwined destinies
to the end—seizing ecstasy, unforgettable adventure—and
love.

A Dell Book   **$3.50**   **(11515-9)**